Lesson
Assessment
Book 2

Annotated Teacher's Edition

Level 1

 SRA

McGraw Hill SRA

A Division of The *McGraw-Hill* Companies

SRAonline.com

 SRA

The *McGraw-Hill* Companies

Table of Contents

Imagine It! Lesson Assessment Book 2

Lesson Assessment Book 2 is an integral part of a complete assessment program that aligns with the instruction in *Imagine It! Lesson Assessment Book 2* covers material from Units 7–10. The skills featured in lesson assessments are tied to reading success and reflect both state and national standards.

Lesson Assessment Book 2 offers the opportunity for summative and formative assessment. As students complete each lesson, they will be assessed on their understanding of the instructional content and the literature in each lesson. The results of the assessments will then be used to inform subsequent instruction. How students score on the assessments offers a picture of current student achievement status while also guiding you toward appropriate instructional decisions.

Each lesson assessment offers you the ability to gauge students' understanding of and growth in the following areas:

• Vocabulary
• Comprehension
• Grammar, Usage, and Mechanics
• Phonics
• Oral Fluency
• Writing

Lesson Assessments

The lesson assessments consist of the following:

Lesson Area	Format	Scope	Scoring
Vocabulary	Multiple Choice	Selection Vocabulary	4 points (2 questions x 2 point)
Comprehension	Multiple Choice	Comprehension Skills	18 points (6 questions x 3 point)
	Short Answer	Comprehension Skills	5 points (1 question x 5 points)
	Personal Response (Short Answer)	General comprehension	3 points (0-3 rubrics)
Phonics	Multiple Choice	Phonics elements practiced in the lesson	10 points (5 questions x 2 point)
Grammar, Usage, and Mechanics	Multiple Choice	Grammar, Usage, and Mechanics skills practiced in the lesson	10 points (5 questions x 2 point)
Oral Fluency	Teacher-Directed Student Performance	Oral fluency development from lesson to lesson	Accuracy Rate on 100-point scale

Students will be graded on their understanding of the vocabulary, comprehension, phonics, and grammar, usage, and mechanics skills taught in the lesson on a 50-point scale. A score of 80% (or 40 points out of 50) or higher on each lesson assessment is expected. Students may look back at the selection to answer the assessment questions. Students who consistently fall below 80% should be monitored for possible intervention. Students who are consistent low-performers in one or more aspects of the lesson assessment should be offered more practice in this lesson area during Workshop.

The Oral Fluency Assessments are scored separately. These assessments offer further data on student abilities. Student performance on oral fluency assessments is often a reliable predictor of student growth and understanding in other lesson areas. Students with consistently low accuracy rates and below-level words per minute numbers should be provided extra fluency practice during Workshop.

End of Unit Writing Prompt

Students will encounter a writing prompt at the end of each unit. Each prompt consists of a writing situation, a specific audience, directions for writing, and a checklist students can reference to ensure they receive the best score possible. Rubrics for scoring student work follow each prompt in this book. These rubrics pertain to genre, writing traits, and conventions. Students will be graded on a 20-point scale based on the rubrics—four points multiplied by five key writing features.

A score of 75% (or 15 points out of 20) or higher on each writing prompt is expected. Students can respond to the prompts in their student workbooks.

Scores and Records

The opening page of each lesson assessment includes a place for students to write their names and the date, and for you to list their scores.

The Oral Fluency Assessment includes a box in which to write the accuracy rate.

The writing prompt includes a place for students to write their names and the date, and for you to list their scores.

Students' scores in the assessment can be registered in the Oral Fluency Scores, Class Assessment Record, and Student Assessment Record pages.

Lesson Assessment Sections

Students may look back at the selection to answer the assessment questions.

Comprehension and Vocabulary

Each comprehension and vocabulary assessment begins with six multiple-choice questions worth three points each. The items reflect the comprehension skills students have been taught specifically in that lesson and skills students have been previously taught.

Then, students are assessed on their knowledge of the selection vocabulary words. The vocabulary assessment is comprised of two multiple-choice questions worth two points each. The questions feature selection vocabulary words from the lessons students have just completed.

Next, students answer one short-answer question worth five points. This question also reflects comprehension skills specific to the lesson and to students' prior knowledge and understanding of comprehension skills. Well-crafted and concise responses that answer the question fully should be awarded five points. Answers that do not fully address the question or are confusing and incomplete should be awarded partial credit, at your discretion. Answers that do not attempt to address the question or provide incorrect information should receive zero points.

Please note the "Possible answer below" following the directions in this Teacher's Edition. This serves as a reminder that students do not have to provide the exact answer shown.

Personal Response

For the Personal Response, students are asked to craft a response related to an idea or thematic issue raised by what they have just read. This section judges students' level of comprehension by assessing their ability to connect what they have just read to a personal level.

These questions are worth three points each. Use the following criteria to judge student responses. To fully answer the question or prompt, student answers should be approximately twenty to thirty words.

Score: 3
The student understands the question and responds suitably using a personal experience, opinion, prior knowledge, or plausible conjecture. The response reflects a thorough comprehension of the selection and is an acceptably complete answer to the question. It has correct spelling, grammar, usage, and mechanics, and it is written neatly and legibly.

Score: 2
The student understands the question and responds using a personal experience, opinion, prior knowledge, or plausible conjecture. The response may reflect partial comprehension of the selection and is a somewhat complete answer to the question. The response is difficult to follow. It has a moderate number of errors in spelling, grammar, usage, and mechanics, and it is mostly written neatly and legibly.

Score: 1
The student has minimal understanding of the question and responds using a personal experience, opinion, prior knowledge, or plausible conjecture. The response may reflect poor comprehension of the selection and is a barely acceptable answer to the question. The response is difficult to follow and may cause the reader to struggle. It has frequent errors in spelling, grammar, usage, and mechanics, and it is written with borderline neatness and legibility.

Score: 0

The student fails to compose a response. If a response is attempted, it is inaccurate, meaningless, or irrelevant. The response may be written so poorly that it is neither legible nor understandable.

The following is an example of a response that would receive a score of "3" if it were written with neatness and legibility. The student shows an understanding of the question. The response focuses on a particular game and describes it. The response has correct spelling, grammar, usage, and mechanics.

SAMPLE

Personal Response *Write about a game you like to play very much.*

I like to play tee ball. It's like baseball. But it isn't as hard. You hit the ball off a tee. You catch it. I like to play with friends.

Phonics Review

Each phonics assessment is comprised of five multiple-choice questions worth two points each. Each question specifically relates to the lesson material for that week.

Grammar, Usage, and Mechanics

Each grammar, usage, and mechanics assessment is comprised of five multiple-choice questions worth two points each. Each question specifically relates to the lesson material for that week. Students sometimes will be asked to identify errors or incorrect constructions, so remind students to read each question carefully.

Oral Fluency Assessments

Administering Oral Fluency Assessments

The Oral Fluency Assessment is an efficient means for evaluating students' ability to read. It is simple to administer and score, yet it provides extraordinarily useful quantitative and qualitative data. You will find oral fluency assessments for each lesson. The words in the selections are of sufficient variety to allow for an analysis of the decoding and vocabulary abilities of a student and to draw inferences about a student's ability to derive meaning from the text.

Make a copy of the Oral Fluency Assessment for each student you will be assessing. Have students turn to the corresponding page in their workbooks. Be sure you have a pen or pencil, a stopwatch or other timer, and extra paper to record any observations. Briefly review the text before you begin. On the Oral Fluency Scores pages, you will record the student's name, the date of the assessment, and the results of the assessment.

Have the student sit comfortably at a table with you. Seat yourself and the student so that you can mark the assessment unobtrusively without distracting the student.

Say: *Here is a selection I would like you to read aloud for me. I am going to listen to you read and take some notes. The notes I take will help me learn how well you can read. You will not be graded for this, so you should not feel nervous. Read the selection carefully and do your best. Take a few minutes now to look over the selection, and then I will tell you when to begin.*

Allow time for the student to preview the story. Be sure you have a pen or pencil.

Say: *Are you ready?* (Check to be sure the student is ready.) *You may begin now.*

Start the timer or watch as the student begins to read. You may pronounce any proper nouns with which the student is unfamiliar. Do not count these words as errors.

Note: If the student becomes frustrated or makes several consecutive errors, stop the assessment.

At the end of one minute place a bracket ( ]) at the end of the last word the student reads.

Scoring Oral Fluency Assessments

The following guidelines will help you score the assessment accurately and consistently.

- Self-correcting should not be counted as an error.
- Repeating the same mistake should be counted as only one error.
- Hesitating for more than five seconds—at which point you would have provided the word—should count as an error.
- Become familiar with the evaluating codes before administering the Oral Fluency Assessment.

Scoring Conventions

- Draw a line through any word that is misread. Count this as an error. If possible, note the type of error. (Misreading *short a* as *short e*, reading *get* as *jet*, and so on).
- Draw a bracket ( ]) at the end of the last word the student reads in one minute.
- Words the student omits should be counted as errors, even if you prompt the student.
- Indicate with a caret extra words that have been inserted. If possible, write the inserted word. Count insertions as errors.
- Draw an arrow between words that have been reversed. Count these as one error.
- Students might repeat words on occasion. Do not count this behavior as an error.

Finding the Student's Accuracy Rate

To find a student's accuracy rate, count the total number of words read in one minute. The numbers beside the passage on the teacher's page will make this an easier task. Subtract the number of errors from the total number of words read and use that figure to find the number of correct words read per minute. Then divide the correct words per minute by the total number of words read to find the accuracy rate. Record these numbers on the Reading Rate and Accuracy chart located on your Oral Fluency Assessment pages.

- Record the student's score on the Oral Fluency Scores pages and the Student Assessment Record.

- Complete the Reading Fluency scale at the bottom of your Oral Fluency Assessment page. These qualitative measures indicate your subjective judgment of how the student compares with other students who are reading at grade level.

READING RATE AND ACCURACY

Total Words Read: <u>67</u>

Number of Errors: <u>11</u>

Number of Correct Words
Read Per Minute (WPM): <u>56</u>

Accuracy Rate: <u>84%</u>

(Number of Correct Words Read per
Minute ÷ Total Words Read)

READING FLUENCY

	Low	Average	High
Decoding ability	○	○	●
Pace	○	●	○
Syntax	○	●	○
Self-correction	○	●	○
Intonation	○	○	●

Interpreting the Oral Fluency Assessments

First, compare the student's number of correct words per minute with the following chart. This will give you an idea of how the student compares with other students in the same grade at the same time of year. The data in this chart represents the approximate number of correct words read per minute a student should be reading. The two rows of numbers represent the 50th and 75th percentiles.

	Units 7-8	Units 9-10	
Grade 1	47	82	75th Percentile
	23	53	50th Percentile

Source Adapted from Hasbrouck, J., & Tindal, G. (2005). Oral Reading Fluency: 90 Years of Measurement (Tech. Rep. No. 33). Eugene, Oregon: University of Oregon, College of Education, Behavioral Research and Teaching.

Then examine the student's accuracy rate. Reading accuracy should remain constant or gradually increase within a grade and between grades, until it stabilizes at ninety percent or higher. You may find it helpful to compare a student's accuracy rate after each administration to ensure that it remains constant or increases.

Next, examine the types of errors the student is making and consider how they represent underlying student behaviors. Here are some examples:

- Inserting extra words suggests that the student understands what is read, is constructing meaning, but is reading somewhat impulsively.

- A student who refuses to attempt to read a word is probably uncertain of his or her abilities and is unwilling to take risks.

- Misreading regular letter sounds implies that the student has not yet mastered the conventions of the sound-symbol relationship. This is in contrast with the student who misreads complex letter sounds (alternate sounds, blends, diphthongs, digraphs, and so on) but has little difficulty with regular letter sounds.

Finally, consider the error pattern. If errors are scattered randomly throughout the passage, then the error types represent skills the student has not yet developed. If errors increase in frequency from beginning to end, then fatigue or inattention likely are involved.

Other Considerations

Several strategies are available for promoting reading fluency and accuracy. These involve pairing an accomplished reader with a developing reader, small-group choral reading, and repeated readings of familiar text.

You may find it useful to establish targets for reading accuracy. These targets may include goals such as reading ten words in a row without error, increasing by increments the number of correct words a student reads in a minute, or decreasing a specific error type. Establishing such targets allows you to provide appropriate instructional support and gives students a reasonable goal.

End of Unit Writing Prompt

The writing prompt offers the opportunity for an on-demand writing performance. Use the rubrics that follow the prompts to judge students' work. Student writing should be included in each student's Writing Portfolio.

Teacher Records

This Teacher's Edition contains record keeping material that will help you keep track of student progress in lesson assessments.

Six Point Rubrics

Six Point Writing Rubrics for assessing student writing are included.

These can take the place of the four point rubrics if you are in a school that uses the six point rubric system.

Oral Fluency Scores

These pages allow you to note student accuracy rates throughout the year.

Class Assessment Record

These pages offer a warehouse for class scores.

The spaces following the student's name allow for the recording of student scores in each lesson assessment (out of the 50-point scale) and each writing prompt (using the four point or six point rubrics to assess).

The format of the Class Assessment Record provides an easy way to monitor student growth across the year.

Student Assessment Record

You can duplicate this page for each student and use it to track student progress.

Comprehension Observation Log

Observing students as they read anthology selections is an effective way to learn their strengths and areas of need in comprehension. Use the Comprehension Observation Log to record your observations of students. Choose a small set of students to focus on for a particular lesson. You might want to observe students more than once to get a clear idea of their comprehension of texts. Copy this page for each student or group of students you observe.

Name _____ Date _____ Score _____

The Kite

Comprehension and Vocabulary

Read the following questions carefully. Then completely fill in the bubble of each correct answer. You may look back at the selection to find the answer to each of the questions.

1. You know this story is not real because
   - Ⓐ toads can not hop.
   - Ⓑ kites can not fly.
   - Ⓒ animals can not talk.
   - Ⓓ birds do not land in bushes.

2. What is Toad's job?
   - Ⓐ to hold the ball of string
   - Ⓑ to hold the kite and run
   - Ⓒ to fix the broken kite
   - Ⓓ to sell the kite and string

3. What do the robins mean when they say the kite is junk?
   - Ⓐ The kite can fly high.
   - Ⓑ The kite is big and funny.
   - Ⓒ The kite is too fancy.
   - Ⓓ The kite is like trash.

The Kite (continued)

4. Why do Frog and Toad go to the meadow?
   Ⓐ The wind is strong there.
   Ⓑ The robins are there.
   Ⓒ The kite is very big.
   Ⓓ The string is very long.

5. What happens last in the story?
   Ⓐ The robins fly out of the bush.
   Ⓑ Frog and Toad sit and watch the kite.
   Ⓒ The kite falls to the ground.
   Ⓓ Toad runs back across the meadow.

6. The robins tell Toad that
   Ⓐ the bush is in the way.
   Ⓑ the string is too short.
   Ⓒ the kite will not fly.
   Ⓓ Frog is teasing him.

The Kite (continued)

7. Frog and Toad were in a **meadow.** What is a **meadow?**

Ⓐ a grassy field

Ⓑ a deep hole

Ⓒ a small pond

Ⓓ a big bush

8. The **kite** fell with a thud. What is a **kite?**

Ⓐ a pretty bug

Ⓑ a kind of plane

Ⓒ a flying toy

Ⓓ a small bird

Read the following question carefully. Use a complete sentence to answer the question. Possible answer below

9. Why do the robins laugh?

The robins laughed because the kite did not fly.

10. Personal Response Frog and Toad worked hard to fly the kite. Write about something that you worked hard to do.

_____

_____

_____

_____

The Kite (continued)

Phonics Review

Fill in the bubble under the word that fits in the blank and is spelled correctly.

Teacher: Fill in the bubble under the word that fits in the blank and is spelled correctly.

Teacher: Can we go <u>now</u>? Fill in the bubble under <u>now</u>.

1. Can we go _____?

noa	noi	nou	now
○	○	○	●

Teacher: This is Pat's <u>house</u>. Fill in the bubble under <u>house</u>.

2. This is Pat's _____.

hoase	house	hoise	howse
○	●	○	○

Teacher: Dad's <u>knee</u> is sore. Fill in the bubble under <u>knee</u>.

3. Dad's _____ is sore.

knee	nee	snee	bnee
●	○	○	○

Teacher: Sue lives <u>down</u> the street. Fill in the bubble under <u>down</u>.

4. Sue lives _____ the street.

down	doon	doen	doun
●	○	○	○

Teacher: The cat is <u>out</u>. Fill in the bubble under <u>out</u>.

5. The cat is _____?

uot	oot	out	oet
○	○	●	○

The Kite • **Lesson Assessment Book 2**

The Kite (continued)

Grammar, Usage, and Mechanics

Read each item. Fill in the bubble for the answer you think is correct.

1. In which sentence are commas used correctly?
   - Ⓐ I have a ball, bat and glove.
   - ⬤Ⓑ I have a ball, bat, and glove.
   - Ⓒ I have, a ball bat and glove.
   - Ⓓ I, have a, ball bat and, glove.

2. In which sentence are quotation marks used correctly?
   - ⬤Ⓐ Mary asked, "Will you go?"
   - Ⓑ Mary asked, "Will you go?
   - Ⓒ "Mary asked," Will you go?
   - Ⓓ Mary "asked," Will you go?

3. In which sentence are quotation marks used correctly?
   - Ⓐ The zoo is open, Mr. Toms said.
   - Ⓑ "The zoo is open, Mr. Toms said.
   - ⬤Ⓒ "The zoo is open," Mr. Toms said.
   - Ⓓ The zoo is open, "Mr. Toms said."

4. In which sentence are quotation marks used correctly?
   - ⬤Ⓐ "Come here," Tina said.
   - Ⓑ Come here," Tina said."
   - Ⓒ Come here, Tina said.
   - Ⓓ "Come here, Tina said.

5. In which sentence are quotation marks used correctly?
   - Ⓐ Mom said, Clean your room now.
   - ⬤Ⓑ Mom said, "Clean your room now."
   - Ⓒ "Mom said," Clean your room now.
   - Ⓓ Mom said, Clean your room "now."

The Kite (continued)

Oral Fluency Assessment

At the Museum

"Please, hurry," Rona said.   1–4
Aunt Dawn smiled. "I know what you want to see. You want   5–16
to see the mummies."   17–20
Rona shook her head. "No. Mummies are okay, but that's not   21–31
what I want to see."   32–36
Aunt Dawn kept thinking. Each time, Rona shook her head.   37–46
Then Aunt Dawn said, "I can't think of anything else."   47–56
"You know what it is? Think of all the books I have at home." 57–70
Aunt Dawn stopped to think. Then she smiled. "I know what   71–80
it is." She took Rona's hand.   81–87
They went downstairs. The room they went into had huge   88–97
bones and skeletons.   98–100
Rona smiled. "This is it. I love dinosaurs!"   101–108

**EVALUATING CODES
FOR ORAL FLUENCY**

sky   (/) words read incorrectly

blue
 ^   sky   (^) inserted word
             ( ]) after the last word

READING RATE AND ACCURACY

Total Words Read: _____

Number of Errors: _____

Number of Correct Words
Read Per Minute (WPM):   _____

Accuracy Rate: _____

(Number of Correct Words Read per
Minute ÷ Total Words Read)

READING FLUENCY

	Low	Average	High
Decoding ability	○	○	○
Pace	○	○	○
Syntax	○	○	○
Self-correction	○	○	○
Intonation	○	○	○

Record student rates on the Oral Fluency Scores pages.

Name _____ Date _____ Score _____

The Little Engine That Could/Riddles

Comprehension and Vocabulary

Read the following questions carefully. Then completely fill in the bubble of each correct answer. You may look back at the selection to find the answer to each of the questions.

1. Why does the train stop?
- Ⓐ People need to get off.
- Ⓑ The toys need to get off.
- Ⓒ The engine is not working.
- Ⓓ The mountain is too tall to climb.

2. The cars of the train do NOT carry
- Ⓐ dolls.
- Ⓑ toy trucks.
- Ⓒ food.
- Ⓓ people.

3. What color is the flag the clown waves at the Shiny New Engine?
- Ⓐ red
- Ⓑ yellow
- Ⓒ green
- Ⓓ blue

The Little Engine That Could/Riddles (continued)

4. What happens right after the Little Blue Engine sees the clown?

Ⓐ She goes on ahead for help.

Ⓑ She stops at once.

Ⓒ The toys get off the train.

Ⓓ The children wake up.

5. How do we know that this story is not real?

Ⓐ Trains do not pull logs.

Ⓑ Toys do not talk.

Ⓒ Children do not like lollypops.

Ⓓ Trains do not go up mountains.

6. "Riddles" says the best riddles make you

Ⓐ thirsty.

Ⓑ hungry.

Ⓒ tired.

Ⓓ think.

The Little Engine That Could/Riddles (continued)

7. The **dining car** is a room on a train where

   Ⓐ meals are served and eaten.

   Ⓑ tickets are collected.

   Ⓒ coal is stored.

   Ⓓ people go to sleep.

8. Fine means about the same as

   Ⓐ tall.

   Ⓑ blue.

   Ⓒ good.

   Ⓓ sad.

Read the following question carefully. Use a complete sentence to answer the question. Possible answer below

9. How do we know the Little Blue Engine is friendly?

We know she is friendly because she stops for the clown.

10. Personal Response Write about a time when you tried your best.

_____

_____

_____

_____

The Little Engine That Could/Riddles (continued)

Phonics Review

Fill in the bubble under the word that fits in the blank and is spelled correctly.

Teacher: Fill in the bubble under the word that fits in the blank and is spelled correctly.

Teacher: Ann saw a movie last night. Fill in the bubble under saw.

1. Ann _____ a movie last night.

swa	saw	suw	sau
○	●	○	○

Teacher: Mom bought a new car. Fill in the bubble under bought.

2. Mom _____ a new car.

bouhgt	boght	baught	bought
○	○	○	●

Teacher: Deb caught the ball. Fill in the bubble under caught.

3. Deb _____ the ball.

caught	cawht	cuaght	cought
●	○	○	○

Teacher: Can the baby crawl? Fill in the bubble under crawl.

4. Can the baby _____?

criwl	craul	crawl	crewl
○	○	●	○

Teacher: Tim ran because he was late. Fill in the bubble under because.

5. Tim ran _____ he was late.

becawse	becuase	becaise	because
○	○	○	●

The Little Engine That Could/Riddles (continued)

Grammar, Usage, and Mechanics

Read each item. Fill in the bubble for the answer you think is correct.

1. In which sentence is a pronoun underlined?
   - (A) The cat plays <u>with</u> it.
   - (C) The cat plays with <u>it</u>.
   - (B) The cat <u>plays</u> with it.
   - (D) <u>The</u> cat plays with it.

2. Which sentence has a singular pronoun?
   - (A) I liked that movie.
   - (B) They went to the park.
   - (C) When will we pick apples?
   - (D) Ms. Cruz spoke to us.

3. Which sentence has a plural pronoun?
   - (A) We had a test today.
   - (B) He did not know the answer.
   - (C) Is she coming?
   - (D) The dog sat near him.

4. Which pronoun can replace the underlined part in the sentence?

   <u>Alice and Sony</u> ran the race.
   - (A) He
   - (C) They
   - (B) She
   - (D) I

5. Which pronoun can replace the underlined part in the sentence?

   Antonio kicked <u>the ball</u>.
   - (A) I
   - (C) we
   - (B) they
   - (D) it

The Little Engine That Could/Riddles (continued)

Oral Fluency Assessment

Pam's Big Day

Today was Pam's birthday. Her mom was working	1–8
in the kitchen.	9–11
"Will you play with me?" Pam asked.	12–18
"Not now," Mom said.	19–22
Dad was in the basement. The door was closed.	23–31
"Don't come down now," Dad said.	32–37
"Will you play with me?" Pam asked her brother.	38–46
"Not now," Jon said. "I'm going to the store."	47–55
"Can I go with you?" Pam asked.	56–62
"Not this time," Jon said.	63–67
Pam was sad. She went to her room. She was bored.	68–78
An hour later, the doorbell rang. Pam ran downstairs.	79–87
Her friend, Hank, was there. So were her friends Meg, Ron,	88–98
and Amy.	99–100
"Surprise!" they shouted.	101–103
Mom brought out a cake. Dad showed up with gifts.	104–113
Jon opened a bag. Inside were party hats and games.	114–123
"Happy Birthday, Pam!" everyone shouted.	124–128

EVALUATING CODES FOR ORAL FLUENCY

sky   (/) words read incorrectly

blue
^   sky   (^) inserted word
           ( ]) after the last word

READING RATE AND ACCURACY

Total Words Read: _____

Number of Errors: _____

Number of Correct Words
Read Per Minute (WPM): _____

Accuracy Rate: _____

(Number of Correct Words Read per
Minute ÷ Total Words Read)

READING FLUENCY

	Low	Average	High
Decoding ability	○	○	○
Pace	○	○	○
Syntax	○	○	○
Self-correction	○	○	○
Intonation	○	○	○

Record student rates on the Oral Fluency Scores pages.

Name _____ Date _____ Score _____

The Itsy Bitsy Spider/The Hare and the Tortoise

Comprehension and Vocabulary

Read the following questions carefully. Then completely fill in the bubble of each correct answer. You may look back at the selection to find the answer to each of the questions.

1. What happens right after the sun comes out?
- Ⓐ The cat falls asleep.
- Ⓑ The spider climbs a chair.
- Ⓒ The rain dries up.
- Ⓓ The fan turns off.

2. Which of these does the spider NOT climb?
- Ⓐ the waterspout
- Ⓑ the yellow pail
- Ⓒ the fan
- Ⓓ the maple tree

3. What makes the spider fall off the wall in the kitchen?
- Ⓐ the cat
- Ⓑ the rain
- Ⓒ the dew
- Ⓓ the fan

The Itsy Bitsy Spider/The Hare and the Tortoise (continued)

4. What do we know about the spider?

Ⓐ The spider is always hungry.

Ⓑ The spider does not give up.

Ⓒ The spider is very big.

Ⓓ The spider likes to swim.

5. Who starts the race in "The Hare and the Tortoise"?

Ⓐ a bear

Ⓑ a raccoon

Ⓒ a fox

Ⓓ a mouse

6. How does the tortoise win?

Ⓐ He takes a shortcut.

Ⓑ He rides in a car.

Ⓒ He starts a long time before the hare.

Ⓓ He passes the hare as he slept.

The Itsy Bitsy Spider/The Hare and the Tortoise (continued)

7. The hare went off at a great **pace. Pace** means

Ⓐ speed.

Ⓑ color.

Ⓒ sound.

Ⓓ size.

8. The spider spins a **silky** web. Something **silky** is

Ⓐ soft and smooth.

Ⓑ big and bumpy.

Ⓒ hard and slippery.

Ⓓ heavy and cold.

Read the following question carefully. Use a complete sentence to answer the question. Possible answer below

9. Why does the spider rest in the sun?

The spider rests in the sun because she has finished her web.

10. **Personal Response** Write about a time you had to keep trying at something.

_____

_____

_____

_____

The Itsy Bitsy Spider/The Hare and the Tortoise (continued)

Phonics Review

Fill in the bubble under the word that fits in the blank and is spelled correctly.

Teacher: Fill in the bubble under the word that fits in the blank and is spelled correctly.

Teacher: Don't make too much <u>noise</u>. Fill in the bubble under <u>noise</u>.

1. Don't make too much _____.

noyse	niose	nouse	noise
○	○	○	●

Teacher: Beth had a new <u>toy</u>. Fill in the bubble under <u>toy</u>.

2. Beth had a new _____.

tey	toy	toiy	toi
○	●	○	○

Teacher: Did you <u>write</u> a letter? Fill in the bubble under <u>write</u>.

3. Did you _____ a letter?

write	rhite	hrite	whrite
●	○	○	○

Teacher: Grandma is on the <u>phone</u>. Fill in the bubble under <u>phone</u>.

4. Grandma is on the _____.

fone	plone	phone	bhone
○	○	●	○

Teacher: The <u>boy</u> played football. Fill in the bubble under <u>boy</u>.

5. The _____ played football.

boy	bey	boi	bou
●	○	○	○

The Itsy Bitsy Spider/The Hare and the Tortoise (continued)

Grammar, Usage, and Mechanics

Read each item. Fill in the bubble for the answer you think is correct.

1. In which sentence is a possessive pronoun underlined?

Ⓐ The story was in her <u>book</u>.

Ⓑ The story was <u>in</u> her book.

Ⓒ <u>The</u> story was in her book.

Ⓓ The story was in <u>her</u> book.

2. In which sentence is a possessive pronoun underlined?

Ⓐ His bike is a lot like <u>that</u>.

Ⓑ His bike is a <u>lot</u> like that.

Ⓒ <u>His</u> bike is a lot like that.

Ⓓ His <u>bike</u> is a lot like that.

3. In which sentence is a possessive pronoun underlined?

Ⓐ My school is in <u>town</u>.

Ⓑ <u>My</u> school is in town.

Ⓒ My <u>school</u> is in town.

Ⓓ My school is <u>in</u> town.

4. In which sentence is a possessive pronoun underlined?

Ⓐ The <u>dog</u> played with its tail.

Ⓑ The dog played <u>with</u> its tail.

Ⓒ The dog played <u>its</u> tail.

Ⓓ The dog played with its <u>tail</u>.

5. In which sentence is a possessive pronoun underlined?

Ⓐ Glen <u>can</u> borrow my hat.

Ⓑ Glen can borrow my <u>hat</u>.

Ⓒ Glen can borrow <u>my</u> hat.

Ⓓ Glen can <u>borrow</u> my hat.

The Itsy Bitsy Spider/The Hare and the Tortoise (continued)

Oral Fluency Assessment

Bike Ride

"What's the matter?" Lin asked.	1–5
"Everyone is riding bikes. I want to go, too," Nate said. "But I	6–18
can't ride without training wheels. No one else still has them."	19–29
"Have you tried to ride without them?" Lin asked.	30–38
Nate shook his head. "I'm too scared."	39–45
"Come on," said Lin. "I'll help you try."	46–53
Lin took off the wheels and helped Nate ride. Every day after	54–65
school, Lin worked with Nate. One day, Nate got on his bike	66–77
and rode all by himself. Lin clapped and cheered.	78–86
The next day, Nate said to his friends, "Let's ride bikes."	87–97
"That sounds like fun," Zach said.	98–103
Everyone else agreed. Nate hurried home to get his bike.	104–113

**EVALUATING CODES
FOR ORAL FLUENCY**

sky   (/) words read incorrectly

blue

^   sky   (^) inserted word

           ( ]) after the last word

READING RATE AND ACCURACY

Total Words Read: _____

Number of Errors: _____

Number of Correct Words
Read Per Minute (WPM):   _____

Accuracy Rate: _____

(Number of Correct Words Read per
Minute ÷ Total Words Read)

READING FLUENCY

	Low	Average	High
Decoding ability	○	○	○
Pace	○	○	○
Syntax	○	○	○
Self-correction	○	○	○
Intonation	○	○	○

Record student rates on the Oral Fluency Scores pages.

Name _____ **Date** _____ **Score** _____

Winners Never Quit!

Comprehension and Vocabulary

Read the following questions carefully. Then completely fill in the bubble of each correct answer. You may look back at the selection to find the answer to each of the questions.

1. What sport does Mia love most of all?
   - (A) basketball
   - (B) baseball
   - (C) soccer
   - (D) hockey

2. Why does Mia's team cheer?
   - (A) Mia agrees to play.
   - (B) Mia scores a goal.
   - (C) Lovdy catches the ball.
   - (D) Garrett picks Mia for his team.

3. Why does Mia quit?
   - (A) All of the other kids are much bigger.
   - (B) Her sister begs her to quit.
   - (C) The ball is too soft for her.
   - (D) She would rather quit than lose.

Winners Never Quit! (continued)

4. What happens the next day right when Mia runs outside?
   Ⓐ The game has already started.
   Ⓑ It begins to rain.
   Ⓒ Garrett picks her for his team.
   Ⓓ Mia scores a goal.

5. What does Mia learn?
   Ⓐ It is a lot of fun to score goals.
   Ⓑ Soccer is a lot of work.
   Ⓒ Playing is more important than winning.
   Ⓓ She is better at baseball than at soccer.

6. What does Mia hate?
   Ⓐ playing baseball
   Ⓑ blocking kicks
   Ⓒ scoring a goal
   Ⓓ losing

Winners Never Quit! (continued)

7. Mia **stomped.** This means that she

(A) kicked a ball.

(B) went inside.

(C) walked heavily.

(D) waited for the game to end.

8. Rather means

(A) not.

(B) more gladly.

(C) always.

(D) less time.

Read the following question carefully. Use a complete sentence to answer the question. Possible answer below

9. What does it mean to dribble a soccer ball?

When you dribble a soccer ball, you kick it again and again.

10. Personal Response Write about a game you like to play very much.

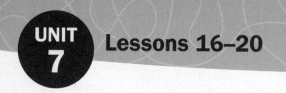

Winners Never Quit! (continued)

Phonics Review

Fill in the bubble under the word that fits in the blank and is spelled correctly.

Teacher: Fill in the bubble under the word that fits in the blank and is spelled correctly.

Teacher: Min <u>heard</u> them call. Fill in the bubble under <u>heard</u>.

1. Min _____ them call.

haerd	heird	heard	herrd
○	○	●	○

Teacher: Ken needs <u>money</u> for lunch. Fill in the bubble under <u>money</u>.

2. Ken needs _____ for lunch.

monay	money	monee	moniy
○	●	○	○

Teacher: The <u>boat</u> is sailing off. Fill in the bubble under <u>boat</u>.

3. The _____ is sailing off.

buot	boet	bot	boat
○	○	○	●

Teacher: Jen ran in the <u>race</u>. Fill in the bubble under <u>race</u>.

4. Jen ran in the _____.

race	rass	rece	rasc
●	○	○	○

Teacher: The farmer has a <u>mule</u>. Fill in the bubble under <u>mule</u>.

5. The farmer has a _____.

muol	muule	mule	muwl
○	○	●	○

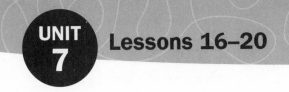

Winners Never Quit! (continued)

Grammar, Usage, and Mechanics

Read each item. Fill in the bubble for the answer you think is correct.

1. In which sentence is an adjective underlined?
   - Ⓐ The green grass grew in the <u>field</u>.
   - Ⓑ The green <u>grass</u> grew in the field.
   - Ⓒ The green grass <u>grew</u> in the field.
   - Ⓓ The <u>green</u> grass grew in the field.

2. In which sentence is an adjective underlined?
   - Ⓐ Five birds <u>sat</u> in a tree.
   - Ⓑ <u>Five</u> birds sat in a tree.
   - Ⓒ Five birds sat in a <u>tree</u>.
   - Ⓓ Five <u>birds</u> sat in a tree.

3. In which sentence is an adjective underlined?
   - Ⓐ Pam wore a pretty <u>dress</u> to the party.
   - Ⓑ Pam <u>wore</u> a pretty dress to the party.
   - Ⓒ Pam wore a <u>pretty</u> dress to the party.
   - Ⓓ Pam wore a pretty dress to the <u>party</u>.

4. Which sentence has a comparative adjective?
   - Ⓐ The smaller puppy is mine.
   - Ⓑ Did you go with him to the zoo?
   - Ⓒ We will go to the new store today.
   - Ⓓ A brown log floated in the water.

5. Which sentence has a comparative adjective?
   - Ⓐ Mom went to work.
   - Ⓑ The green frog jumped into the lake.
   - Ⓒ Kim is taller than Ben.
   - Ⓓ This book is about the moon.

Winners Never Quit! (continued)

Oral Fluency Assessment

New School

School would start tomorrow. Paul had just moved. He didn't	1–10
know anyone at his new school.	11–16
That night, Dad asked, "Are you afraid?"	17–23
Paul nodded. "I don't know anyone. And I never rode a	24–34
bus before."	35–36
"Do you remember being afraid to start kindergarten?"	37–44
Dad asked.	45–46
Paul had felt sick then, too. "Yes," Paul whispered.	47–55
Dad hugged him. "What happened?"	56–60
"The first day I met Will and Sam. Ana shared her lunch	61–72
with me. We all became friends." Paul smiled.	73–80
Dad smiled, too. "What do you think will happen tomorrow?"	81–90
Paul thought, and said, "Will the same thing happen?"	91–99
"I bet it will," Dad said and kissed Paul good night.	100–110

**EVALUATING CODES
FOR ORAL FLUENCY**

sky   (/) words read incorrectly

blue
^   sky   (^) inserted word
            ( ]) after the last word

READING RATE AND ACCURACY

Total Words Read: _____

Number of Errors: _____

Number of Correct Words
Read Per Minute (WPM): _____

Accuracy Rate: _____

(Number of Correct Words Read per
Minute ÷ Total Words Read)

READING FLUENCY

	Low	Average	High
Decoding ability	○	○	○
Pace	○	○	○
Syntax	○	○	○
Self-correction	○	○	○
Intonation	○	○	○

Record student rates on the Oral Fluency Scores pages.

Name _____ **Date** _____ **Score** _____

Writing Prompt

Narrative Writing

Writing Situation

A time when you did something difficult

Audience

Your classmates

Directions for Writing

Think about a time when you had to try hard to succeed. It can be in school, sports, or anything else that you did. Write about what you did, how you did it, and what made you keep trying.

Checklist

You will earn the best score if you

- think about your ideas before you start writing.
- stay on topic.
- have a good beginning, middle, and end to your story.
- use describing words.
- use action words.
- tell about the place where the story happens.
- write complete sentences.
- use words that tell how you feel.
- use correct capital letters, end marks, and spelling.
- read your writing after you finish and check for mistakes.

Four Point Rubrics for Narrative Writing

Genre	1 Point	2 Points	3 Points	4 Points
Narrative	Narrative has missing details or elements. Order and narrative structure are lacking. Plot is unclear. Character development is not apparent. Setting does not include descriptions of where and when the narrative is set.	Narrative includes plot outline and some descriptive details, but narrative structure is not entirely clear. Character development is minimal. Setting includes minimal descriptions.	Narrative includes fairly well developed plot. Narrative structure is clear. Characters are developed, though some characters may seem superficial. Setting includes description.	Narrative includes complex, organized plot line(s). Narrative structure is well defined. Characters well defined throughout. Setting includes detailed descriptions.
Narrative: Theme	No theme is apparent.	Superficial theme is included but not integrated.	A theme is expressed but not well developed.	The narrative fully develops a theme that expresses an underlying message beyond the narrative plot.
Writing Traits				
Audience	Displays little or no sense of audience.	Displays some sense of audience.	Writes with audience in mind throughout.	Displays a strong sense of audience. Engages audience.
Voice	The writing provides little sense of voice.	The voice is either inappropriately personal or inappropriately impersonal.	A voice is present, though in places, the writing is less expressive, engaging, or sincere.	The writer has chosen a voice appropriate for the topic, purpose, and audience.
Writing Conventions				
Conventions Overall	Demonstrates little evidence of standard writing conventions.	Demonstrates limited but inconsistent control of standard writing conventions.	Demonstrates emerging, consistent use of standard writing conventions such as capitalization and end punctuation.	Demonstrates consistent use and awareness of standard writing conventions.

Name _____ Date _____ Score _____

How a Seed Grows

Comprehension and Vocabulary

Read the following questions carefully. Then completely fill in the bubble of each correct answer. You may look back at the selection to find the answer to each of the questions.

1. Which of these does NOT grow from seeds?
Ⓐ apple tree
Ⓑ bird
Ⓒ corn
Ⓓ clover

2. What do you do right after you make a hole in the soil?
Ⓐ Fill in the hole.
Ⓑ Put water on the soil.
Ⓒ Write a number on the shell.
Ⓓ Put one seed in the hole.

3. Why can't you see the seeds begin to grow?
Ⓐ They are too small.
Ⓑ They do not have enough water.
Ⓒ They are under the soil.
Ⓓ They are broken.

How a Seed Grows (continued)

4. Which of these is a kind of bean?
   Ⓐ pole
   Ⓑ clover
   Ⓒ wheat
   Ⓓ apple

5. Why were twelve seeds planted in the story?
   Ⓐ so we can start a garden
   Ⓑ so we can see the seeds grow
   Ⓒ so we can get many plants
   Ⓓ so we can use many beans

6. How are all seeds alike?
   Ⓐ All seeds make beans.
   Ⓑ All seeds are very tiny.
   Ⓒ All seeds need soil to grow.
   Ⓓ All seeds are good to eat.

How a Seed Grows (continued)

7. The growing seed pushes soil **aside. Aside** means

   Ⓐ to one side.

   Ⓑ to the inside.

   Ⓒ into the air.

   Ⓓ into the ground.

8. The **root** grows from one part of the bean seed. What is a **root?**

   Ⓐ a kind of bean

   Ⓑ a part of a plant which grows into the ground

   Ⓒ a part of a plant which holds up the leaves

   Ⓓ a small insect

Read the following question carefully. Use a complete sentence to answer the question. Possible answer below

9. What is the difference between how an oak tree grows and how a bean plant grows?

   An oak tree grows slowly. A bean plant grows quickly.

10. Personal Response Write about a garden you know. It can be your garden or a garden you have seen.

How a Seed Grows (continued)

Phonics Review

Fill in the bubble under the word that fits in the blank and is spelled correctly.

Teacher: Fill in the bubble under the word that fits in the blank and is spelled correctly.

Teacher: Did they <u>wax</u> the floors? Fill in the bubble under <u>wax</u>.

1. Did they _____ the floors?

wix	wex	wax	wox
○	○	●	○

Teacher: This is the <u>same</u> book I read. Fill in the bubble under <u>same</u>.

2. This is the _____ book I read.

same	saam	samm	saim
●	○	○	○

Teacher: The officer has a <u>badge</u>. Fill in the bubble under <u>badge</u>.

3. The officer has a _____.

bedge	bidge	bodge	badge
○	○	○	●

Teacher: The rice came in a <u>sack</u>. Fill in the bubble under <u>sack</u>.

4. The rice came in a _____.

saack	sack	soack	seck
○	●	○	○

Teacher: It looks like <u>rain</u>. Fill in the bubble under <u>rain</u>.

5. It looks like _____.

ran	rian	rain	raine
○	○	●	○

How a Seed Grows (continued)

Grammar, Usage, and Mechanics

Read each item. Fill in the bubble for the answer you think is correct.

1. Which of these is a telling sentence?
   - Ⓐ What day is today?
   - Ⓑ Who is coming tomorrow?
   - Ⓒ Lin swims in the lake.
   - Ⓓ This is a great game!

2. Which of these is a telling sentence?
   - Ⓐ How many children are there?
   - Ⓑ Mike climbs a tall tree.
   - Ⓒ Where is the door?
   - Ⓓ When will we leave?

3. Which of these is an asking sentence?
   - Ⓐ Give your brother a turn.
   - Ⓒ Jan rides her bike.
   - Ⓑ Whose book is this?
   - Ⓓ Kick it over here!

4. Which of these is an asking sentence?
   - Ⓐ Is Lisa at home?
   - Ⓑ The tiger hid in the grass.
   - Ⓒ Do not drop that!
   - Ⓓ That is a funny story.

5. Which of these is an asking sentence?
   - Ⓐ Dad washed the dishes.
   - Ⓑ Don't forget your coat!
   - Ⓒ Is that hat mine?
   - Ⓓ Paul set the table.

How a Seed Grows (continued)

Oral Fluency Assessment

At the Library

Dana loved the library. Mom and Dad took her to there every	1–12
Saturday. Dana got to choose her own books.	13–20
One day, Dana found a good book. She showed her mom	21–31
the book.	32–33
"Look," Dana said. "It's *Little House in the Big Woods.*"	34–43
Mom said, "I loved that book when I was a little girl."	44–55
Dana was surprised. "You read this book?" she said.	56–64
"But you're old!"	65–67
Mom laughed. "Yes, but that book is older."	68–75
Dana turned to her father and asked, "What books did you	76–86
like to read?"	87–89
Dad said, "I read books about sports. Then I read adventure	90–100
books. I still like to read books like that."	101–109
Mom laughed and said, "I guess that means you never	110–119
grew up."	120–121

**EVALUATING CODES
FOR ORAL FLUENCY**

sky   (/) words read incorrectly

blue

^   sky   (^) inserted word

        ( ]) after the last word

READING RATE AND ACCURACY

Total Words Read: _____

Number of Errors: _____

Number of Correct Words
Read Per Minute (WPM): _____

Accuracy Rate: _____

(Number of Correct Words Read per
Minute ÷ Total Words Read)

READING FLUENCY

	Low	Average	High
Decoding ability	O	O	O
Pace	O	O	O
Syntax	O	O	O
Self-correction	O	O	O
Intonation	O	O	O

Record student rates on the Oral Fluency Scores pages.

Name _____ **Date** _____ **Score** _____

The Garden/Saguaro

Comprehension and Vocabulary

Read the following questions carefully. Then completely fill in the bubble of each correct answer. You may look back at the selection to find the answer to each of the questions.

1. Which of these does Toad NOT try so his seeds will grow?
   - Ⓐ digging them up
   - Ⓑ shouting at them
   - Ⓒ playing music for them
   - Ⓓ reading poems to them

2. What does Toad want to have?
   - Ⓐ a home
   - Ⓑ a garden
   - Ⓒ a tree
   - Ⓓ a meal

3. Why do Toad's seeds not grow when he wants them to grow?
   - Ⓐ He has not given them enough water.
   - Ⓑ The seeds are dead.
   - Ⓒ The seeds he planted are not real.
   - Ⓓ He has not waited long enough.

The Garden/Saguaro (continued)

4. Why does Toad fall asleep?
   Ⓐ He ran a long way.
   Ⓑ He ate a big meal.
   Ⓒ He worked hard.
   Ⓓ Frog makes him take a nap.

5. A saguaro is a kind of
   Ⓐ animal.
   Ⓑ weed.
   Ⓒ cactus.
   Ⓓ tree.

6. What is inside a saguaro?
   Ⓐ water
   Ⓑ sand
   Ⓒ dirt
   Ⓓ rocks

The Garden/Saguaro (continued)

7. "**Quite** soon," said Frog. **Quite** means

   Ⓐ not.

   Ⓑ very.

   Ⓒ later.

   Ⓓ always.

8. Toad **shouted** at his seeds. **Shouted** means

   Ⓐ called loudly.

   Ⓑ planted.

   Ⓒ looked carefully.

   Ⓓ listened.

Read the following question carefully. Use a complete sentence to answer the question. Possible answer below

9. Where does Toad get seeds for his garden?

   Frog gives some seeds to Toad.

10. **Personal Response** Write about something that was hard for you to wait for.

The Garden/Saguaro (continued)

Phonics Review

Fill in the bubble under the word that fits in the blank and is spelled correctly.

Teacher: Fill in the bubble under the word that fits in the blank and is spelled correctly.

Teacher: Wes is very <u>sick</u>. Fill in the bubble under <u>sick</u>.

1. Wes is very _____.

sicke	soick	sick	seck
○	○	●	○

Teacher: That dog is <u>mine</u>. Fill in the bubble under <u>mine</u>.

2. That dog is _____.

mine	mene	minn	mone
●	○	○	○

Teacher: Can Dad <u>fix</u> this? Fill in the bubble under <u>fix</u>.

3. Can Dad _____ this?

fixe	fex	faix	fix
○	○	○	●

Teacher: Please do not <u>cry</u>. Fill in the bubble under <u>cry</u>.

4. Please do not _____.

crie	cre	cra	cry
○	○	○	●

Teacher: The rope was <u>tied</u>. Fill in the bubble under <u>tied</u>.

5. The rope was _____.

taed	tied	tiyd	teid
○	●	○	○

The Garden/Saguaro (continued)

Grammar, Usage, and Mechanics

Read each item. Fill in the bubble for the answer you think is correct.

1. In which sentence is a possessive noun underlined?
   Ⓐ Jen's <u>dog</u> barks loudly.
   Ⓑ <u>Jen's</u> dog barks loudly.
   Ⓒ Jen's dog barks <u>loudly</u>.
   Ⓓ Jen's dog <u>barks</u> loudly.

2. In which sentence is a possessive noun underlined?
   Ⓐ The cat's <u>tail</u> is white.　　**Ⓒ** The <u>cat's</u> tail is white.
   Ⓑ <u>The</u> cat's tail is white.　　Ⓓ The cat's tail is <u>white</u>.

3. Which sentence has a singular possessive pronoun?
   Ⓐ The boy ran down the hill.
   Ⓑ That is her toy.
   Ⓒ The cars are red and black.
   Ⓓ A bug is on the plant.

4. Which sentence has a singular possessive pronoun?
   Ⓐ I lost my bag a few days ago.
   Ⓑ The toys are in the closet.
   Ⓒ Those girls like to climb trees.
   Ⓓ He is looking for the kitten.

5. Which sentence has a plural possessive pronoun?
   Ⓐ The fish swim in the water.
   Ⓑ Horses have strong legs.
   Ⓒ Mom put our lunches in the box.
   Ⓓ The ball rolled down the hill.

The Garden/Saguaro (continued)

Oral Fluency Assessment

A Walk in the Park

It was a nice day. Ben went for a walk in the park.	1–13
The park was near his home. The park has grass and trees.	14–25
There is a pretty lake in the park. There are benches near	26–37
the lake.	38–39
Ben heard a noise. He looked up and saw a nest. It was in a	40–54
tree in the park. Then he saw a pretty bird fly to the tree. The	55–69
bird landed near the nest. Ben hoped there were baby birds in	70–81
the nest. He wanted to see the baby birds grow up. Ben would	82–94
come back to the park again to see the baby birds.	95–105

**EVALUATING CODES
FOR ORAL FLUENCY**

sky (/) words read incorrectly

blue
^ sky (^) inserted word
( ]) after the last word

READING RATE AND ACCURACY

Total Words Read: _____

Number of Errors: _____

Number of Correct Words
Read Per Minute (WPM): _____

Accuracy Rate: _____

(Number of Correct Words Read per
Minute ÷ Total Words Read)

READING FLUENCY

	Low	Average	High
Decoding ability	○	○	○
Pace	○	○	○
Syntax	○	○	○
Self-correction	○	○	○
Intonation	○	○	○

Record student rates on the Oral Fluency Scores pages.

Name _____ **Date** _____ **Score** _____

Green and Growing

Comprehension and Vocabulary

Read the following questions carefully. Then completely fill in the bubble of each correct answer. You may look back at the selection to find the answer to each of the questions.

1. Which of these is NOT a plant?

- Ⓐ a tree
- Ⓑ a shrub
- Ⓒ a butterfly
- Ⓓ a vine

2. How are all green growing things alike?

- Ⓐ They all make their own food.
- Ⓑ They all move around to find water.
- Ⓒ They all have cones.
- Ⓓ They all have stems.

3. What is the smallest plant on Earth?

- Ⓐ redwood
- Ⓑ cedar
- Ⓒ cattail
- Ⓓ duckweed

Green and Growing (continued)

4. Which of these are parts of a plant?
   - Ⓐ roots, leaves
   - Ⓑ fir, cedar
   - Ⓒ poppies, daisies
   - Ⓓ cactus, reed

5. Where does a lily of the valley grow best?
   - Ⓐ on a rocky hill
   - Ⓑ in a cool, dark place
   - Ⓒ on a mountain slope
   - Ⓓ in a hot, dry desert

6. A way plants move is by
   - Ⓐ bending away from ice.
   - Ⓑ sliding down hills.
   - Ⓒ growing toward sunlight.
   - Ⓓ jumping into water.

Green and Growing (continued)

7. Plants give us **energy. Energy** is
   - Ⓐ a fancy flower.
   - Ⓑ the air we breathe.
   - Ⓒ the strength to do something.
   - Ⓓ a kind of wood.

8. A **shrub** is a kind of
   - Ⓐ bush.
   - Ⓑ pond.
   - Ⓒ food.
   - Ⓓ paper.

Read the following question carefully. Use a complete sentence to answer the question. Possible answer below

9. How tall can a giant redwood tree be?

   It can be as tall as a twenty-story skyscraper.

10. **Personal Response** What plants do you like?

   _____

   _____

   _____

   _____

   _____

Green and Growing (continued)

Phonics Review

Fill in the bubble under the word that fits in the blank and is spelled correctly.

Teacher: Fill in the bubble under the word that fits in the blank and is spelled correctly.

Teacher: look at the big <u>rock</u>! Fill in the bubble under <u>rock</u>.

1. Look at that big _____!

rock	rocke	reck	ruck
●	○	○	○

Teacher: Put out fire with the <u>hose</u>. Fill in the bubble uner <u>hose</u>.

2. Put out the fire with the _____.

hoss	hose	hise	hase
○	●	○	○

Teacher: What is in this <u>box</u>? Fill in the bubble under <u>box</u>.

3. What is in this _____?

boxe	bax	box	bix
○	○	●	○

Teacher: Mom cut the <u>loaf</u> of bread. Fill in the bubble under <u>loaf</u>.

4. Mom cut the _____ of bread.

loaf	liaf	leif	luaf
●	○	○	○

Teacher: It is time to go <u>home</u>. Fill in the bubble under <u>home</u>.

5. It is time to go _____.

homm	hame	hime	home
○	○	○	●

Green and Growing (continued)

Grammar, Usage, and Mechanics

Read each item. Fill in the bubble for the answer you think is correct.

1. Which word means about the same as <u>bake</u>?

   (A) eat   (C) cook

   (B) fly   (D) swim

2. Which word means about the same as <u>discover</u>?

   (A) find

   (B) run

   (C) send

   (D) drive

3. Which word means about the same as <u>tiny</u>?

   (A) sick

   (B) small

   (C) true

   (D) large

4. Which word means about the same as <u>start</u>?

   (A) turn

   (B) hide

   (C) begin

   (D) read

5. Which word means about the same as <u>beautiful</u>?

   (A) small

   (B) pretty

   (C) happy

   (D) wet

Green and Growing (continued)

Oral Fluency Assessment

Best Friends

A man and his dog were in the park. They were playing in   1–13
a large, grassy field. The man threw the ball. The dog ran after   14–26
the ball. The dog brought the ball back to the man. The dog   27–39
wagged its tail. It was having a lot of fun. The man looked like   40–53
he was having fun, too.   54–58

The man and the dog finished playing their game. Then they   59–69
went for a walk. The dog was very good. He walked right next   70–82
to the man. The dog did not pull at the leash. All the people who   83–97
saw them could tell that they were happy. They could see that   98–109
the man and the dog were best friends.   110–117

**EVALUATING CODES
FOR ORAL FLUENCY**

sky   (/) words read incorrectly

blue
  ^   sky   (^) inserted word
           ( ]) after the last word

READING RATE AND ACCURACY

Total Words Read: _____

Number of Errors: _____

Number of Correct Words
Read Per Minute (WPM):   _____

Accuracy Rate: _____

(Number of Correct Words Read per
Minute ÷ Total Words Read)

READING FLUENCY

	Low	Average	High
Decoding ability	○	○	○
Pace	○	○	○
Syntax	○	○	○
Self-correction	○	○	○
Intonation	○	○	○

Record student rates on the Oral Fluency Scores pages.

Name _____ Date _____ Score _____

Flowers/Flowers at Night

Comprehension and Vocabulary

Read the following questions carefully. Then completely fill in the bubble of each correct answer. You may look back at the selection to find the answer to each of the questions.

1. Plants need flowers to make
   - Ⓐ roots.
   - Ⓑ seeds.
   - Ⓒ stems.
   - Ⓓ bugs.

2. Flowers begin as
   - Ⓐ buds.
   - Ⓑ roots.
   - Ⓒ sticks.
   - Ⓓ leaves.

3. Birds and bugs both use flowers to
   - Ⓐ hide in them.
   - Ⓑ drink nectar from them.
   - Ⓒ make perfume from them.
   - Ⓓ match the color of them.

Flowers/Flowers at Night (continued)

4. Where do the flowers of a plant grow?
   Ⓐ under the ground
   Ⓑ on the roots
   Ⓒ at the end of a stem
   Ⓓ inside a seed

5. The first part of "Flowers at Night" is about flowers that
   Ⓐ are yellow.
   Ⓑ close up at night.
   Ⓒ bugs like.
   Ⓓ grow very tall.

6. Flowers in the poem are compared to
   Ⓐ rainbows.
   Ⓑ pretty feathers.
   Ⓒ open windows.
   Ⓓ butterflies.

Flowers/Flowers at Night (continued)

7. Flowers are **bright. Bright** is another word for

Ⓐ smelly.

Ⓑ large.

Ⓒ beautiful.

Ⓓ colorful.

8. Flowers have **petals.** What are **petals**?

Ⓐ the part of a flower that has color

Ⓑ the part of the flower that holds it up

Ⓒ the part of the flower that makes seeds

Ⓓ the part of the flower that takes in sunlight

Read the following question carefully. Use a complete sentence to answer the question. Possible answer below

9. What is true about all of the flowers on one plant?

All of the flowers on one plant are the same.

10. Personal Response Where can you see pretty flowers where you live?

_____

_____

_____

_____

Flowers/Flowers at Night (continued)

Phonics Review

Fill in the bubble under the word that fits in the blank and is spelled correctly.

Teacher: Fill in the bubble under the word that fits in the blank and is spelled correctly.

Teacher: Laura wished us <u>luck</u>. Fill in the bubble under <u>luck</u>.

1. Laura wished us _____.

leck	lucke	lyck	luck
○	○	○	●

Teacher: Do you want an ice <u>cube</u>? Fill in the bubble under <u>cube</u>.

2. Do you want an ice _____?

cabe	cuub	cube	cibe
○	○	●	○

Teacher: Mary could not <u>budge</u> the log. Fill in the bubble under <u>budge</u>.

3. Mary could not _____ the log.

budge	bedge	bidge	bodje
●	○	○	○

Teacher: There are a <u>few</u> grapes left . Fill in the bubble under <u>few</u>.

4. There are a _____ grapes left.

fu	few	fue	faw
○	●	○	○

Teacher: May I play some <u>music</u> now? Fill in the bubble under <u>music</u>.

5. May I play some _____ now?

mesic	masic	mosic	music
○	○	○	●

Flowers/Flowers at Night (continued)

Grammar, Usage, and Mechanics

Read each item. Fill in the bubble for the answer you think is correct.

1. Which word means the opposite of <u>hard</u>?
   - Ⓐ easy
   - Ⓑ small
   - Ⓒ pretty
   - Ⓓ fast

2. Which word means the opposite of <u>leave</u>?
   - Ⓐ see
   - Ⓑ laugh
   - Ⓒ come
   - Ⓓ drop

3. Which word means the opposite of <u>young</u>?
   - Ⓐ old
   - Ⓑ mad
   - Ⓒ lost
   - Ⓓ hard

4. Which word means the opposite of <u>less</u>?
   - Ⓐ kind
   - Ⓑ more
   - Ⓒ nice
   - Ⓓ funny

5. Which word means the opposite of <u>good</u>?
   - Ⓐ free
   - Ⓑ tall
   - Ⓒ bad
   - Ⓓ dry

Flowers/Flowers at Night (continued)

Oral Fluency Assessment

Brownie's Turn

It was a warm day. The sun was shining. Dot was playing	1–12
outside. She saw her friend, Ken. This gave her an idea.	13–23
"Do you want to play tag?" asked Dot. Ken said he did. They	24–36
looked for more friends. That way the game would be more fun.	37–48
They went to Pat's house. She said she would play. Her	49–59
brother, Mark, wanted to play, too.	60–65
The four children went to Dot's yard. They were all set to	66–77
play. Then Ken's dog, Brownie, ran into the yard. The children	78–88
laughed. Brownie wanted to play tag with them, too.	89–97

**EVALUATING CODES
FOR ORAL FLUENCY**

sky　　　　(/) words read incorrectly

blue
 ^　sky　　(^) inserted word
　　　　　　( ]) after the last word

READING RATE AND ACCURACY

Total Words Read: 　　＿＿＿

Number of Errors: 　　＿＿＿

Number of Correct Words
Read Per Minute (WPM): 　＿＿＿

Accuracy Rate: 　　＿＿＿

(Number of Correct Words Read per
Minute ÷ Total Words Read)

READING FLUENCY

	Low	Average	High
Decoding ability	○	○	○
Pace	○	○	○
Syntax	○	○	○
Self-correction	○	○	○
Intonation	○	○	○

Record student rates on the Oral Fluency Scores pages.

Name _____ **Date** _____ **Score** _____

Plants That Eat Animals

Comprehension and Vocabulary

Read the following questions carefully. Then completely fill in the bubble of each correct answer. You may look back at the selection to find the answer to each of the questions.

1. Where do most plants get what they need to grow?
   - Ⓐ from the air
   - **Ⓑ from the soil**
   - Ⓒ from its flowers
   - Ⓓ from people

2. What do the leaves of a Venus flytrap look like?
   - Ⓐ a bat's wing
   - Ⓑ a cat's tail
   - **Ⓒ a clam's shell**
   - Ⓓ a dog's nose

3. What happens right after an insect touches the hairs on a Venus flytrap leaf?
   - **Ⓐ The halves of the leaf snap shut.**
   - Ⓑ The leaf gives off a sweet smell.
   - Ⓒ The plant grows very tall.
   - Ⓓ The plant removes minerals from the insect.

Plants That Eat Animals (continued)

4. What makes the hairs on a sundew leaf fold over?

Ⓐ rain falling on the plant

Ⓑ sun hitting the plant

Ⓒ an insect getting stuck on the plant

Ⓓ a person touching the plant

5. Why is the insect stuck in the pitcher plant?

Ⓐ It cannot climb back up the slippery sides.

Ⓑ The liquid inside the plant is sticky.

Ⓒ A leaf of the plant folds over.

Ⓓ The plant sucks the insect inside.

6. Which of these is a plant that eats animals?

Ⓐ a bladderwort

Ⓑ a tulip

Ⓒ a bamboo

Ⓓ a dandelion

Plants That Eat Animals (continued)

7. Some plants live in **wetlands. Wetlands** are

   Ⓐ mountains.

   Ⓑ deserts.

   Ⓒ forests.

   Ⓓ swamps.

8. The leaf gives off a sweet juice that **insects** like.
   Insects are

   Ⓐ animals with fur.

   Ⓑ fish with scales.

   Ⓒ bugs with six legs.

   Ⓓ animals with long tails.

Read the following question carefully. Use a complete sentence to answer the question. Possible answer below

9. How did the pitcher plant get its name?

   It is shaped like a pitcher and holds liquid like a pitcher.

10. **Personal Response** What plant do you like best? Why do you like it?

   _____

   _____

   _____

   _____

Plants That Eat Animals (continued)

Phonics Review

Fill in the bubble under the word that fits in the blank and is spelled correctly.

Teacher: Fill in the bubble under the word that fits in the blank and is spelled correctly.

Teacher: Dan took a <u>bite</u> of the apple. Fill in the bubble under <u>bite</u>.

1. Dan took a _____ of the apple.

bite	bote	baite	biit
●	○	○	○

Teacher: Wash the dishes with <u>soap</u>. Fill in the bubble under <u>soap</u>.

2. Wash the dishes with _____.

seop	soop	soap	soip
○	○	●	○

Teacher: The boys <u>hope</u> to go fishing. Fill in the bubble under <u>hope</u>.

3. The boys _____ to go fishing.

hop	hupe	hape	hope
○	○	○	●

Teacher: Some pigs are <u>huge</u>. Fill in the bubble under <u>huge</u>.

4. Some pigs are _____.

houg	huge	hage	hige
○	●	○	○

Teacher: A cat will <u>chase</u> a mouse. Fill in the bubble under <u>chase</u>.

5. A cat will _____ a mouse.

chese	chase	chaas	chise
○	●	○	○

Lessons 21–25

Plants That Eat Animals (continued)

Grammar, Usage, and Mechanics

Read each item. Fill in the bubble for the answer you think is correct.

1. Which of these means the same as <u>is not</u>?
   - Ⓐ it's
   - Ⓑ can't
   - Ⓒ isn't
   - Ⓓ hasn't

2. Which of these means the same as <u>we will</u>?
   - Ⓐ we've
   - Ⓑ we're
   - Ⓒ we'll
   - Ⓓ she'll

3. Which of these means the same as <u>they are</u>?
   - Ⓐ he's
   - Ⓑ they're
   - Ⓒ that's
   - Ⓓ here's

4. Which of these means the same as <u>wasn't</u>?
   - Ⓐ would not
   - Ⓑ will not
   - Ⓒ was not
   - Ⓓ were not

5. Which of these means the same as <u>I'm</u>?
   - Ⓐ I am
   - Ⓑ I will
   - Ⓒ I did
   - Ⓓ I might

Plants That Eat Animals (continued)

Oral Fluency Assessment

Worming Around

Worms live underground most of the time. They dig holes   1–10
deep in the ground. The holes help plants grow. The holes help   11–22
worms, too. They give the worms a place to hide.   23–32

Sometimes worms come out of the ground at night. They do   33–43
this on warm, wet nights. You might see worms on the ground   44–55
after a spring rain. They like the ground to be wet.   56–66

Birds like to eat worms. They look for the worms early in the   67–79
day. Did you ever hear someone say, "The early bird gets the   80–91
worm"? That's where this saying comes from.   92–98

**EVALUATING CODES
FOR ORAL FLUENCY**

sky   (/) words read incorrectly

blue
^   sky   (^) inserted word
              ( ]) after the last word

READING RATE AND ACCURACY

Total Words Read: _____

Number of Errors: _____

Number of Correct Words
Read Per Minute (WPM):   _____

Accuracy Rate: _____

(Number of Correct Words Read per
Minute ÷ Total Words Read)

READING FLUENCY

	Low	Average	High
Decoding ability	○	○	○
Pace	○	○	○
Syntax	○	○	○
Self-correction	○	○	○
Intonation	○	○	○

Record student rates on the Oral Fluency Scores pages.

Name _____ **Date** _____ **Score** _____

Writing Prompt

Expository Writing

Writing Situation

A tree or other plant near where you live

Audience

A friend or family member your age who lives in a different place

Directions for Writing

Think about a tree or other plant near where you live. It can be a huge tree in a park, a plant with flowers near where you live, or any other plant that you know. Write about the plant in a way that will help the person who reads your story understand what the plant looks like and what is interesting about it.

Checklist

You will earn the best score if you

- choose a plant that you know well.
- think about the plant before you start writing.
- remember who will read about your plant.
- use describing words to tell about the plant.
- write paragraphs that have a topic sentence and focus on related ideas.
- write complete sentences.
- use words that tell how you feel about the plant.
- use correct capital letters, end marks, and spelling.
- read your writing after you finish and check for mistakes.

Four Point Rubrics for Expository Writing

Genre	1 Point	2 Points	3 Points	4 Points
Expository	Composition has no introduction or clear topic. It offers a group of loosely related facts or a series of poorly written steps. No conclusion is included.	Composition is clearly organized around main points with supportive facts or assertions. Composition has no clear introduction, but its topic is identifiable. However, it includes many facts unrelated to the topic, or it describes things in a disorganized way. No conclusion is included.	Main points and supportive details can be identified, but they are not clearly marked. Composition has an introduction and offers facts about the topic. Some facts may be irrelevant, or some ideas may be vague or out of order. The report is fairly well organized but doesn't have a strong conclusion.	Traces and constructs a line of argument, identifying part-to-whole relations. Main points are supported with logical and appropriate evidence. Composition begins with an introduction and offers relevant facts about the topic or describes the topic appropriately. The report is organized using cause/effect, comparison/contrast, or another pattern. It ends with a strong conclusion.
Writing Traits				
Ideas/Content	Superficial and/or minimal content is included.	Main ideas are understandable, although they may be overly broad or simplistic. Supporting detail is limited.	Main ideas are easily understandable. Support is present, although it may be limited or rather general.	Main ideas stand out and are developed by strong support and rich details.
Elaboration (supporting details and examples that develop the main idea)	Little or no elaboration or detail	Minimal detail.	Includes sufficient detail to develop or support ideas.	Elaborates on ideas with supporting details.
Focus	No focus is present. Main idea cannot be inferred.	Topic/position/direction is unclear and must be inferred.	Topic/position is stated and direction/purpose is previewed and maintained. Mainly stays on topic.	Topic/position is clearly stated, previewed, and maintained. Topics and details are tied together.
Writing Conventions				
Conventions Overall	Demonstrates little evidence of standard writing conventions.	Demonstrates limited but inconsistent control of standard writing conventions.	Demonstrates emerging, consistent use of standard writing conventions such as capitalization and end punctuation.	Demonstrates consistent use and awareness of standard writing conventions.

Name _____ Date _____ Score _____

Homes

Comprehension and Vocabulary

Read the following questions carefully. Then completely fill in the bubble of each correct answer. You may look back at the selection to find the answer to each of the questions.

1. What is a home in the Arctic made of?

Ⓐ clay and mud

Ⓑ snow and ice

Ⓒ sticks and branches

Ⓓ cloth and blankets

2. Why is grass on the roof of a house woven tightly?

Ⓐ to keep out rain

Ⓑ to keep out sunshine

Ⓒ to keep the house cool

Ⓓ to keep birds from getting in

3. What is the same about all homes?

Ⓐ They are made of wood.

Ⓑ They are easy to build.

Ⓒ They give us shelter.

Ⓓ They can be carried.

Homes (continued)

4. Which of these would be good to use to build a home you could move easily?
   Ⓐ ice
   Ⓑ clay
   Ⓒ blankets
   Ⓓ bricks

5. What would be a problem for a home made of packed mud?
   Ⓐ wind
   Ⓑ rain
   Ⓒ heat
   Ⓓ cold

6. What is the same about what people use to make their homes?
   Ⓐ They use cement.
   Ⓑ They use expensive tools.
   Ⓒ They use only wood.
   Ⓓ They use what is at hand.

Homes (continued)

7. Homes in the desert are made of **clay.** What is **clay?**
   - Ⓐ soft, sticky mud
   - Ⓑ animal skins
   - Ⓒ sand and rocks
   - Ⓓ the inside of a cactus

8. Good houses are **sturdy.** What does **sturdy** mean?
   - Ⓐ pretty
   - Ⓑ tall
   - Ⓒ wide
   - Ⓓ strong

Read the following question carefully. Use a complete sentence to answer the question. Possible answer below

9. Why do people who move from place to place have simple homes?

   <u>These people have to be able to build their homes quickly.</u>

10. **Personal Response** Write about your home and what you like most about it.

   _____

   _____

   _____

   _____

Homes (continued)

Phonics Review

Fill in the bubble under the word that fits in the blank and is spelled correctly.

Teacher: Fill in the bubble under the word that fits in the blank and is spelled correctly.

Teacher: Let's go out on the <u>deck</u>. Fill in the bubble under <u>deck</u>.

1. Let's go out on the _____.

decke	dack	deeke	deck
○	○	○	●

Teacher: We heard a <u>beep</u>. Fill in the bubble under <u>beep</u>.

2. We heard a _____.

bep	beep	bapp	bipe
○	●	○	○

Teacher: The children rode <u>ponies</u>. Fill in the bubble under <u>ponies</u>.

3. The children rode _____.

ponies	ponees	poneis	ponais
●	○	○	○

Teacher: It's Ron's turn <u>next</u>. Fill in the bubble under <u>next</u>.

4. It's Ron's turn _____.

next	naxt	noxt	nixt
●	○	○	○

Teacher: Bees make <u>honey</u>. Fill in the bubble under <u>honey</u>.

5. Bees make _____.

honie	honay	honey	honee
○	○	●	○

Homes • **Lesson Assessment Book 2**

Homes (continued)

Grammar, Usage, and Mechanics

Read each item. Fill in the bubble for the answer you think is correct.

1. Which sentence is in the present tense?
   - (A) Emma feeds her dog.
   - (B) Her dog wanted more food.
   - (C) Emma walked her dog.
   - (D) The dog liked the walk.

2. Which sentence is in the present tense?
   - (A) The man chopped the tree.
   - (B) Ron plays in the park.
   - (C) The flowers looked pretty.
   - (D) A rabbit hopped on the log.

3. Which sentence is in the past tense?
   - (A) Finn runs in a race.
   - (B) Mary swims in the pool.
   - (C) Bill jumped over a rock.
   - (D) Tina throws a ball.

4. Which sentence is in the past tense?
   - (A) Three children played tag.
   - (B) My brother helps Dad clean.
   - (C) My sister rakes the leaves.
   - (D) Our friend says hello.

5. Which sentence is in the past tense?
   - (A) Mom works in the garden.
   - (B) We planted peas and beans.
   - (C) Dads pulls out weeds.
   - (D) Leaves grow on the trees.

Homes (continued)

Oral Fluency Assessment

Socks and String

Socks heard a loud noise. He was afraid.   1–8
He ran under the bed and hid. He did not want to come out.   9–22
"I'm sorry," said Kim. She looked under the bed at her kitten.   23–34
"I dropped my book. Please don't be afraid."   35–42
Socks did not understand Kim. He did not know what she   43–53
was saying. He was still afraid. He did not want to come out   54–66
from under the bed.   67–70
Kim had an idea. She got a piece of string. The string was   71–83
Socks's favorite toy. Quick as a wink, Socks forgot he was   84–94
afraid. He wanted to play with the string.   95–102

<table>
<tr><td colspan="2">EVALUATING CODES
FOR ORAL FLUENCY</td></tr>
<tr><td>sky</td><td>(/) words read incorrectly</td></tr>
<tr><td>blue
^ sky</td><td>(^) inserted word
( ]) after the last word</td></tr>
</table>

READING RATE AND ACCURACY

Total Words Read:	_____
Number of Errors:	_____
Number of Correct Words Read Per Minute (WPM):	_____
Accuracy Rate:	_____

(Number of Correct Words Read per Minute ÷ Total Words Read)

READING FLUENCY

	Low	Average	High
Decoding ability	○	○	○
Pace	○	○	○
Syntax	○	○	○
Self-correction	○	○	○
Intonation	○	○	○

Record student rates on the Oral Fluency Scores pages.

Name _____ **Date** _____ **Score** _____

Homes Around the World/Building a House

Comprehension and Vocabulary

Read the following questions carefully. Then completely fill in the bubble of each correct answer. You may look back at the selection to find the answer to each of the questions.

1. What kind of home folds up?
Ⓐ a pueblo
Ⓑ a tent
Ⓒ a reed hut
Ⓓ a house on stilts

2. What are all the homes in this story used for?
Ⓐ All of them float.
Ⓑ All of them are on wheels.
Ⓒ All of them are for living.
Ⓓ All of them are made of plants

3. In Mali, houses are cool on hot days because
Ⓐ they have windows.
Ⓑ they are built in cliffs.
Ⓒ they have water all around.
Ⓓ they do not have roofs.

Homes Around the World/Building a House (continued)

4. A window is most like

Ⓐ a wheel.

Ⓑ a door.

Ⓒ a fireplace.

Ⓓ a roof.

5. Who helps build a house?

Ⓐ a cook

Ⓑ a teacher

Ⓒ a plumber

Ⓓ a nurse

6. How is an electrician like a plumber?

Ⓐ They do their jobs after the roof is on.

Ⓑ The walls need to be up before they can do their jobs.

Ⓒ The house needs to be painted before they can do their jobs.

Ⓓ They do their jobs before the cement is poured.

Homes Around the World/Building a House (continued)

7. Sidewalks are made of **cement.** What is **cement?**

Ⓐ the new roof

Ⓑ big pieces of wood

Ⓒ sand, water, and rock

Ⓓ a kind of wire

8. A **porch** is a nice place to sit. A **porch** is

Ⓐ a place covered with flowers.

Ⓑ the back of a floating home.

Ⓒ for people to smile out of.

Ⓓ an entrance covered with a roof.

Read the following question carefully. Use a complete sentence to answer the question. Possible answer below

9. Why do people have windows?

Windows are for letting in light and letting people see out.

10. Personal Response What kind of house do you want to live in? Why?

_____

_____

_____

_____

Homes Around the World/Building a House (continued)

Phonics Review

Fill in the bubble under the word that fits in the blank and is spelled correctly.

Teacher: Fill in the bubble under the word that fits in the blank and is spelled correctly.

Teacher: Beth took one step. Fill in the bubble under step.

1. Beth took one _____.

| snep | step | shep | slep |
| ○ | ● | ○ | ○ |

Teacher: Her cat is black. Fill in the bubble under black.

2. Her cat is _____.

| brack | blak | black | blask |
| ○ | ○ | ● | ○ |

Teacher: We saw a crab by the sea. Fill in the bubble under crab.

3. We saw a _____ by the sea.

| crab | clab | srab | chab |
| ● | ○ | ○ | ○ |

Teacher: Do not drip the paint. Fill in the bubble under drip.

4. Do not _____ the paint.

| brip | dlip | dhip | drip |
| ○ | ○ | ○ | ● |

Teacher: What is your plan? Fill in the bubble under plan.

5. What is your _____?

| plan | phan | slan | pran |
| ● | ○ | ○ | ○ |

Homes Around the World/Building a House (continued)

Grammar, Usage, and Mechanics

Read each item. Fill in the bubble for the answer you think is correct.

1. Which sentence is in the past tense?
   - Ⓐ Dad carried the big box.
   - Ⓑ The box has a bow on it.
   - Ⓒ It is a present for Grandma.
   - Ⓓ Grandma lives near us.

2. Which sentence is in the past tense?
   - Ⓐ The baby cried for its bottle.
   - Ⓑ The mother holds the baby.
   - Ⓒ The baby drinks juice.
   - Ⓓ The father helps, too.

3. Which sentence is in the past tense?
   - Ⓐ Amy's cat sits on her lap.
   - Ⓑ Kitty reads a book.
   - Ⓒ Jon ate his cereal.
   - Ⓓ Fran listens to the radio.

4. Which sentence is in the past tense?
   - Ⓐ Aaron saw his father.
   - Ⓑ Jim talks to us on the phone.
   - Ⓒ Aunt Rita cooks breakfast.
   - Ⓓ The phone rings.

5. Which sentence is in the past tense?
   - Ⓐ The lion sleeps in the sun.
   - Ⓑ The tiger roared at a mouse.
   - Ⓒ The monkey hangs in a tree.
   - Ⓓ The bear looks for fish.

Homes Around the World/Building a House (continued)

Oral Fluency Assessment

The Circus Comes Home

Lynn's friends invited her to go to the circus. It was in a big
tent. The tent was full of people. There was music playing.

Three large rings were in the middle of the tent. There were
acts in each ring. Lynn did not know where to look first. She
loved the bears. Her friends liked the clowns best.

The next day, the girls played circus. They put a sheet on
chairs. This was their tent. They made believe they were part of
the acts. Some girls were clowns. Others were animals. Lynn's
mom made them snacks. She said they had a great circus. She
asked if she could watch.

1–14
15–25
26–37
38–50
51–59
60–71
72–83
84–93
94–105
106–110

**EVALUATING CODES
FOR ORAL FLUENCY**

sky (/) words read incorrectly

blue
  ^ sky (^) inserted word
        ( ]) after the last word

READING RATE AND ACCURACY

Total Words Read: _____

Number of Errors: _____

Number of Correct Words
Read Per Minute (WPM): _____

Accuracy Rate: _____

(Number of Correct Words Read per
Minute ÷ Total Words Read)

READING FLUENCY

	Low	Average	High
Decoding ability	○	○	○
Pace	○	○	○
Syntax	○	○	○
Self-correction	○	○	○
Intonation	○	○	○

Record student rates on the Oral Fluency Scores pages.

Name _____ **Date** _____ **Score** _____

The White House/Snail's Pace

Comprehension and Vocabulary

Read the following questions carefully. Then completely fill in the bubble of each correct answer. You may look back at the selection to find the answer to each of the questions.

1. The first president to live in the White House was
   - Ⓐ George Washington.
   - Ⓑ John Adams.
   - Ⓒ Abraham Lincoln.
   - Ⓓ Thomas Jefferson.

2. In which city is the White House?
   - Ⓐ Washington, D.C.
   - Ⓑ New York
   - Ⓒ Philadelphia
   - Ⓓ Boston

3. Where in the White House does the president work?
   - Ⓐ the East Room
   - Ⓑ the Blue Room
   - Ⓒ the Blue Office
   - Ⓓ the Oval Office

The White House/Snail's Pace (continued)

4. What is the name of the largest room in the White House?

 Ⓐ the East Room

 Ⓑ the Blue Room

 Ⓒ the Blue Office

 Ⓓ the Oval Office

5. In the poem, a snail is slow because it

 Ⓐ talks too much.

 Ⓑ carries a house on its back.

 Ⓒ has too many friends.

 Ⓓ likes to rest.

6. The poem says you would be slow if you

 Ⓐ did not study hard.

 Ⓑ ate too much.

 Ⓒ carried your house.

 Ⓓ were tired.

The White House/Snail's Pace (continued)

7. The White House is the most **famous** home in America. Something **famous** is

Ⓐ very far away.

Ⓑ very old.

Ⓒ very well known.

Ⓓ very hard to find.

8. Snails **trudge.** This means they

Ⓐ move slowly.

Ⓑ carry their houses.

Ⓒ are always busy.

Ⓓ are always hungry.

Read the following question carefully. Use a complete sentence to answer the question. Possible answer below

9. Why do so many people visit the White House?

<u>They visit it because it is an</u>

<u>important symbol of the country.</u>

10. Personal Response Would you want to go to the White House? Why or why not?

_____

_____

_____

_____

The White House/Snail's Pace (continued)

Phonics Review

Fill in the bubble under the word that fits in the blank and is spelled correctly.

Teacher: Fill in the bubble under the word that fits in the blank and is spelled correctly.

Teacher: What will they do <u>then</u>? Fill in the bubble under <u>then</u>.

1. What will they do _____?

    tlen   shen   tren   then
    ○   ○   ○   ●

Teacher: Did the <u>ship</u> sail yet? Fill in the bubble under <u>ship</u>.

2. Did the _____ sail yet?

    swip   stip   ship   thip
    ○   ○   ●   ○

Teacher: This is a nice <u>chair</u>. Fill in the bubble under <u>chair</u>.

3. This is a nice _____.

    clair   chair   ckair   thair
    ○   ●   ○   ○

Teacher: Ann and Jon <u>both</u> like sports. Fill in the bubble under <u>both</u>.

4. Ann and Jon _____ like sports.

    both   borh   boch   boht
    ●   ○   ○   ○

Teacher: Paul left <u>when</u> his mother left. Fill in the bubble under <u>when</u>.

5. Paul left _____ his mother left.

    wlen   twen   when   phen
    ○   ○   ●   ○

The White House/Snail's Pace (continued)

Grammar, Usage, and Mechanics

Read each item. Fill in the bubble for the answer you think is correct.

1. Which sentence is in the future tense?

Ⓐ Gina will go soon. Ⓒ Ken ate his lunch.

Ⓑ Pepe rides his bike. Ⓓ Judd carries a ball.

2. Which sentence is in the future tense?

Ⓐ Wes looks out the window.

Ⓑ Paula rode on the train.

Ⓒ Tina will ride on the bus.

Ⓓ Ella picks some flowers.

3. Which sentence is in the future tense?

Ⓐ Our team won the game.

Ⓑ No one lives in that house.

Ⓒ My friends will come to visit.

Ⓓ The bus waits for us.

4. Which sentence is in the future tense?

Ⓐ The bird flies in the air.

Ⓑ The cat jumps to the floor.

Ⓒ Dad will paint the room yellow.

Ⓓ Noel drank his milk.

5. Which sentence is in the future tense?

Ⓐ Leaves fell from the trees.

Ⓑ The weather is cold.

Ⓒ It will snow tonight.

Ⓓ The wind blows the snow.

The White House/Snail's Pace (continued)

Oral Fluency Assessment

Elephants

Elephants can talk. They do not use words like we use. They	1–12
talk in other ways. They move their big ears. They raise their	13–24
long trunks. They wave their trunks in the air.	25–33
They talk with noises they make, too. One loud sound is like	34–45
a trumpet. They lift their trunks in the air. Then they make this	46–58
loud sound. They also make low sounds. The low sound is like a	59–71
cough. Some think it sounds like a grunt.	72–79
Mothers seem to talk to their children. The children talk	80–89
back. We do not know what they are saying. People want to	90–101
learn what these animals mean when they talk.	102–109

**EVALUATING CODES
FOR ORAL FLUENCY**

sky   (/) words read incorrectly

blue
 ^   sky   (^) inserted word
           ( ]) after the last word

READING RATE AND ACCURACY

Total Words Read: _____

Number of Errors: _____

Number of Correct Words
Read Per Minute (WPM): _____

Accuracy Rate: _____

(Number of Correct Words Read per
Minute ÷ Total Words Read)

READING FLUENCY

	Low	Average	High
Decoding ability	○	○	○
Pace	○	○	○
Syntax	○	○	○
Self-correction	○	○	○
Intonation	○	○	○

Record student rates on the Oral Fluency Scores pages.

Name _____ **Date** _____ **Score** _____

Finding Shelter/Home

Comprehension and Vocabulary

Read the following questions carefully. Then completely fill in the bubble of each correct answer. You may look back at the selection to find the answer to each of the questions.

1. A wasp's nest is most like a
   - Ⓐ fish's nest.
   - Ⓑ spider's nest.
   - Ⓒ bird's nest.
   - Ⓓ hornet's nest.

2. What do most creatures need?
   - Ⓐ to find shelter from weather
   - Ⓑ to grow a warm coat
   - Ⓒ to grow their own food
   - Ⓓ to dig for water

3. Some animals look for a safe place in the autumn
   - Ⓐ to hunt.
   - Ⓑ to eat.
   - Ⓒ to fly.
   - Ⓓ to sleep.

Finding Shelter/Home (continued)

4. What do animals in hot places need that is different from animals in cold places?
Ⓐ thick coats
Ⓑ shady places
Ⓒ no food
Ⓓ bright sunshine

5. The poem says a home is more than just
Ⓐ fun.
Ⓑ brick.
Ⓒ shelter.
Ⓓ meal.

6. The poem is supposed to make you feel
Ⓐ tired.
Ⓑ happy.
Ⓒ mad.
Ⓓ hungry.

Finding Shelter/Home (continued)

7. A home is where you go to get **comfort. Comfort** is

Ⓐ a long walk.

Ⓑ a place for a pet.

Ⓒ a good feeling.

Ⓓ a place for a fire.

8. What is **hibernating?**

Ⓐ digging a hole

Ⓑ sleeping through the winter

Ⓒ climbing in a tall tree

Ⓓ going to a place where there is food

Read the following question carefully. Use a complete sentence to answer the question. Possible answer below

9. Why are people very successful animals?

People can live anywhere. They change to go with the weather.

10. **Personal Response** What animal homes are near where you live?

_____

_____

_____

_____

Finding Shelter/Home (continued)

Phonics Review

Fill in the bubble under the word that fits in the blank and is spelled correctly.

Teacher: Fill in the bubble under the word that fits in the blank and is spelled correctly.

Teacher: The horse pulled the <u>cart</u>. Fill in the bubble under <u>cart</u>.

1. The horse pulled the _____.

coart	cart	ceart	cort
○	●	○	○

Teacher: Gene has a new <u>shirt</u>. Fill in the bubble under <u>shirt</u>.

2. Gene has a new _____.

shert	shiirt	sheart	shirt
○	○	○	●

Teacher: This <u>winter</u> has been very cold. Fill in the bubble under <u>winter</u>.

3. This _____ has been very cold.

wintir	winter	wintar	wintur
○	●	○	○

Teacher: The <u>store</u> is not open. Fill in the bubble under <u>store</u>.

4. The _____ is not open.

stoor	stoar	store	stoir
○	○	●	○

Teacher: You should <u>turn</u> at the next corner. Fill in the bubble under <u>turn</u>.

5. You should _____ at the next corner.

turn	toorn	tourn	tirn
●	○	○	○

Finding Shelter/Home (continued)

Grammar, Usage, and Mechanics

Read each item. Fill in the bubble for the answer you think is correct.

1. Which sentence contains a singular noun?
   - Ⓐ The children run and play.
   - Ⓑ Wild animals live in zoos.
   - **Ⓒ** The frog jumped into the water.
   - Ⓓ They are afraid of snakes.

2. Which sentence contains a plural noun?
   - Ⓐ Penny gave her friend a gift.
   - Ⓑ Max played baseball with Deb.
   - **Ⓒ** The girls used their bats.
   - Ⓓ The log burned in the fire.

3. Which sentence contains a possessive noun?
   - **Ⓐ** The kitten's fur is soft.
   - Ⓑ The bird had blue feathers.
   - Ⓒ Zebras are black and white.
   - Ⓓ The room was very quiet.

4. Which sentence contains a pronoun?
   - Ⓐ Nick and Lily met at the corner.
   - **Ⓑ** They went to the park.
   - Ⓒ Nick likes the slide and swings.
   - Ⓓ Saturday is a busy day here.

5. Which sentence contains a possessive pronoun?
   - Ⓐ Those shoes are pink.
   - Ⓒ Anton looked at the rabbits.
   - Ⓑ Leng won two prizes.
   - **Ⓓ** Dad found my glove.

Finding Shelter/Home (continued)

Oral Fluency Assessment

Flowers and You

Flowers come in many colors. They have many shapes.	1–9
Some are so small you can not see them. Others are quite large.	10–22
Bees like flowers. They sip sweet juice from them. Then the	23–33
bees make honey. The bees also help plants grow.	34–42
Flowers turn into fruit on plants. People eat the fruit. Limes	43–53
and pears are types of fruit. There are many kinds of fruit. You	54–66
can see how many when you go to the store.	67–76
Seeds come from fruit. The seeds make more plants grow. If	77–87
there were no flowers and seeds, we would have no new plants.	88–99
And that would not be good for us.	100–107

EVALUATING CODES FOR ORAL FLUENCY

sky   (/) words read incorrectly

blue
^   sky   (^) inserted word
           ( ]) after the last word

READING RATE AND ACCURACY

Total Words Read: _____

Number of Errors: _____

Number of Correct Words
Read Per Minute (WPM):   _____

Accuracy Rate: _____

(Number of Correct Words Read per
Minute ÷ Total Words Read)

READING FLUENCY

	Low	Average	High
Decoding ability	O	O	O
Pace	O	O	O
Syntax	O	O	O
Self-correction	O	O	O
Intonation	O	O	O

Record student rates on the Oral Fluency Scores pages.

Name _____ Date _____ Score _____

This House Is Made of Mud

Comprehension and Vocabulary

Read the following questions carefully. Then completely fill in the bubble of each correct answer. You may look back at the selection to find the answer to each of the questions.

1. Which of these is used to make the mud house?
- Ⓐ wood
- Ⓑ straw
- Ⓒ metal
- Ⓓ rocks

2. How is the house like the Moon?
- Ⓐ Both are made of mud.
- Ⓑ Both have holes.
- Ⓒ Both have mice.
- Ⓓ Both are round.

3. Why are there windows in the house?
- Ⓐ So breezes can pass through
- Ⓑ So animals can get in
- Ⓒ So people can get in
- Ⓓ So light can get out

This House Is Made of Mud (continued)

4. How do the mice get in the house?
   Ⓐ by flying in
   Ⓑ by crawling in
   Ⓒ by people letting them in
   Ⓓ by sliding in

5. The house's yard is
   Ⓐ cool and rocky.
   Ⓑ muddy and wet.
   Ⓒ hot and dry.
   Ⓓ very small.

6. Which of these can you infer from the story?
   Ⓐ The person telling the story does not like the house.
   Ⓑ The house is very famous.
   Ⓒ The house is very old.
   Ⓓ The person telling the story likes the house.

This House Is Made of Mud (continued)

7. The house has **tunnels** under the floor. **Tunnels** are
   - Ⓐ underground passageways.
   - Ⓑ tall fences to keep animals out.
   - Ⓒ strong walls to keep rain out.
   - Ⓓ places for a fire.

8. The family will **share** the house. To **share** means to
   - Ⓐ keep for yourself.
   - Ⓑ sell.
   - Ⓒ give to others.
   - Ⓓ visit.

Read the following question carefully. Use a complete sentence to answer the question. Possible answer below

9. How is the house like our Earth?

   The house is made from the same thing as the Earth.

10. **Personal Response** Write about what your home is made of.

   _____

   _____

   _____

   _____

This House Is Made of Mud (continued)

Phonics Review

Fill in the bubble under the word that fits in the blank and is spelled correctly.

Teacher: Fill in the bubble under the word that fits in the blank and is spelled correctly.

Teacher: The vet will <u>clip</u> the dog's coat. Fill in the bubble under <u>clip</u>.

1. The vet will _____ the dog's coat.

clip	crip	stip	clup
●	○	○	○

Teacher: The family is eating a <u>meal</u>. Fill in the bubble under <u>meal</u>.

2. The family is eating a _____.

mell	meol	meal	mael
○	○	●	○

Teacher: It's time for <u>lunch</u>. Fill in the bubble under <u>lunch</u>.

3. It's time for _____.

lunsh	lunch	lanch	lunck
○	●	○	○

Teacher: The sheep eat grass. Fill in the bubble under <u>sheep</u>.

4. The _____ eat grass.

shep	cheip	shleep	sheep
○	○	○	●

Teacher: Does he like to <u>draw</u>? Fill in the bubble under <u>draw</u>.

5. Does he like to _____?

braw	drau	draw	driw
○	○	●	○

This House Is Made of Mud (continued)

Grammar, Usage, and Mechanics

Read each item. Fill in the bubble for the answer you think is correct.

1. Which sentence is in the present tense?
   - Ⓐ Oscar helps the teacher.
   - Ⓑ Jade mailed a letter.
   - Ⓒ Nan wanted a balloon.
   - Ⓓ Mrs. Miller will come soon.

2. Which sentence is in the past tense?
   - Ⓐ The parade begins now.
   - Ⓑ The mayor rides in a fancy car.
   - Ⓒ The band marched through town.
   - Ⓓ Lots of people watch the parade.

3. Which sentence is in the future tense?
   - Ⓐ The fire trucks will come next.
   - Ⓑ Everybody laughs at the clowns.
   - Ⓒ My brother looked for bikes.
   - Ⓓ These oranges taste sweet.

4. Which sentence is in the past tense?
   - Ⓐ Mom says the house is a mess.
   - Ⓑ Toni cleaned her room.
   - Ⓒ Dad will clean the garage.
   - Ⓓ The house looks nicer now.

5. Which sentence is in the future tense?
   - Ⓐ Helen will have a party.
   - Ⓑ Molly liked the party.
   - Ⓒ Nita wants to come, too.
   - Ⓓ Seth asks if he can go.

This House Is Made of Mud (continued)

Oral Fluency Assessment

Funny Rick

Nan likes music. She plays the guitar. Her dad taught her. He likes to sing when she plays.

Someone else likes the way she plays, too. It is the family dog, Rick. When Nan plays, he makes noises. It sounds like Rick is trying to sing. When he sings, Nan laughs. But Rick just keeps on singing.

Rick does other things that are funny. He loves his ball. If he wants to play, he brings you his ball. At night, he sleeps with his ball. When he goes for a walk, he takes his ball. But if you throw the ball, he will not chase it.

1–11
12–18
19–31
32–41
42–54
55–57
58–70
71–83
84–98
99–106

**EVALUATING CODES
FOR ORAL FLUENCY**

sky ⟍⟋ (/) words read incorrectly

blue
^ sky (^) inserted word
( ]) after the last word

READING RATE AND ACCURACY

Total Words Read: _____

Number of Errors: _____

Number of Correct Words
Read Per Minute (WPM): _____

Accuracy Rate: _____

(Number of Correct Words Read per
Minute ÷ Total Words Read)

READING FLUENCY

	Low	Average	High
Decoding ability	○	○	○
Pace	○	○	○
Syntax	○	○	○
Self-correction	○	○	○
Intonation	○	○	○

Record student rates on the Oral Fluency Scores pages.

Name _____ Date _____ Score _____

Writing Prompt

Persuasive Writing

Writing Situation

How your school can be improved

Audience

The students and teachers in your school

Directions for Writing

Think of something that would make your school better. Explain why this improvement is important and why other people would like it, too.

Checklist

You will earn the best score if you

- think about your ideas before you start writing.
- tell your idea in the first sentence.
- explain why your idea is important.
- stay on the topic.
- write complete sentences.
- use words that tell how you feel about the idea.
- try to make the reader think your idea is a good one.
- repeat your idea in the last sentence.
- use correct capital letters, end marks, and spelling.
- read your writing after you finish and check for mistakes.

Four Point Rubrics for Persuasive Writing

UNIT 9

Genre	1 Point	2 Points	3 Points	4 Points
Persuasive	Position is absent or confusing. Insufficient writing to show that criteria are met.	Position is vague or lacks clarity. Unrelated ideas or multiple positions are included.	An opening statement identifies position. Writing may develop fewer or more points than delineated in opening. Focus may be too broad.	Sets scope and purpose of paper in introduction. Maintains position throughout. Supports arguments. Includes effective closing.
Writing Traits				
Audience	Displays little or no sense of audience.	Displays some sense of audience.	Writes with audience in mind throughout.	Displays a strong sense of audience. Engages audience.
Focus	No focus is present. Main idea cannot be inferred.	Topic/position/direction is unclear and must be inferred.	Topic/position is stated and direction/purpose is previewed and maintained. Mainly stays on topic.	Topic/position is clearly stated, previewed, and maintained. Topics and details are tied together.
Organization	Organization is not apparent.	An attempt has been made to organize the writing, though the writing may be a list of facts or ideas.	Organization is clear and coherent. Beginning or conclusion is included.	Organization develops the central idea. The order and structure move the reader through the text easily. Beginning grabs attention. Conclusion adds impact. Uses paragraphs appropriately.
Writing Conventions				
Conventions Overall	Demonstrates little evidence of standard writing conventions.	Demonstrates limited but inconsistent control of standard writing conventions.	Demonstrates emerging, consistent use of standard writing conventions such as capitalization and end punctuation.	Demonstrates consistent use and awareness of standard writing conventions.

Four Point Rubrics for Persuasive Writing • **Lesson Assessment Book 2**

Name _____ Date _____ Score _____

My Brother Is Afraid of Just About Everything

Comprehension and Vocabulary

Read the following questions carefully. Then completely fill in the bubble of each correct answer. You may look back at the selection to find the answer to each of the questions.

1. How do we know the brother is younger?
   - Ⓐ He does not go to school yet.
   - Ⓑ He is afraid of just about everything.
   - Ⓒ He likes dogs.
   - Ⓓ He screams when water is let out of the tub.

2. The brother thinks the vacuum cleaner is
   - Ⓐ a bear.
   - Ⓑ a shark.
   - Ⓒ a monster.
   - Ⓓ a lion.

3. Where does the brother go during a storm?
   - Ⓐ behind the bushes
   - Ⓑ under the bed
   - Ⓒ into the bathtub
   - Ⓓ in his closet

My Brother Is Afraid of Just About Everything (continued)

4. Why does the brother wrap his arms around the sister?
   Ⓐ He is pretending to be a snake.
   Ⓑ He is afraid of the train.
   Ⓒ He loves the sister very much.
   Ⓓ He needs to hold the sister up.

5. How is the sister like the brother?
   Ⓐ Both are afraid of dogs.
   Ⓑ Both are afraid of the vacuum cleaner.
   Ⓒ Both are afraid of school.
   Ⓓ Both are afraid of something.

6. Why is the brother happy?
   Ⓐ He gets to go to school.
   Ⓑ He sees a dog.
   Ⓒ He sees a train.
   Ⓓ He sees some friends.

My Brother Is Afraid of Just About Everything (continued)

7. Another word for **underneath** is

Ⓐ below.

Ⓑ afraid.

Ⓒ thunderstorm.

Ⓓ away.

8. Trembling means about the same as

Ⓐ jumping.

Ⓑ crying.

Ⓒ smiling.

Ⓓ shaking.

Read the following question carefully. Use a complete sentence to answer the question. Possible answer below

9. Why is the brother afraid of so many things?

The brother thinks the things will hurt him.

10. Personal Response Write about something you are afraid of.

_____

_____

_____

_____

My Brother Is Afraid of Just About Everything (continued)

Phonics Review

Fill in the bubble under the word that fits in the blank and is spelled correctly.

Teacher: Fill in the bubble under the word that fits in the blank and is spelled correctly.

Teacher: This desk is made of <u>wood</u>. Fill in the bubble under <u>wood</u>.

1. This desk is made of _____.

wode	woed	wood	wod
○	○	●	○

Teacher: This is Pam's <u>book</u>. Fill in the bubble under <u>book</u>.

2. This is Pam's _____.

bok	book	boak	bowk
○	●	○	○

Teacher: Tom put the ball in the <u>hoop</u>. Fill in the bubble under <u>hoop</u>.

3. Tom put the ball in the _____.

houp	hupe	hoip	hoop
○	○	○	●

Teacher: Jan's dog got <u>loose</u>. Fill in the bubble under <u>loose</u>.

4. Jan's dog got _____.

loose	loos	loise	lowse
●	○	○	○

Teacher: The plant <u>grew</u> bigger. Fill in the bubble under <u>grew</u>.

5. The plant _____ bigger.

groo	grou	grew	griw
○	○	●	○

My Brother Is Afraid of Just About Everything (continued)

Grammar, Usage, and Mechanics

Read each item. Fill in the bubble for the answer you think is correct.

1. Which sentence has a comparative adjective?

Ⓐ The goats ate the grass.

Ⓑ Many people watch funny movies.

Ⓒ Raoul plays music louder than Beth.

Ⓓ The chair is big and soft.

2. In which sentence is the underlined part correct?

Ⓐ Jane is <u>tall</u> than anyone else in class.

Ⓑ Jane is <u>taller</u> than anyone else in class.

Ⓒ Jane is <u>tallest</u> than anyone else in class.

Ⓓ Jane is <u>more taller</u> than anyone else in class.

3. Which word means about the same as <u>pleased</u>?

Ⓐ strong   Ⓒ glad

Ⓑ afraid   Ⓓ busy

4. Which word means about the same as <u>finish</u>?

Ⓐ ride

Ⓑ end

Ⓒ play

Ⓓ look

5. Which word means the opposite of <u>small</u>?

Ⓐ large

Ⓑ new

Ⓒ hard

Ⓓ weak

My Brother Is Afraid of Just About Everything (continued)

Oral Fluency Assessment

The Noise Outside

Anne and Mr. Rojas went outside. They had heard a strange noise. They looked to see what it was. They could not find anything.

"Let's go back in, Anne. We can look later if we hear the sound again."

"I want to look near that bush. Then I will come in."

Anne went to the bush at the far side of the house. It was dark, and she could not see well. Just then, something furry crawled up against her face. Anne almost jumped out of her skin! Then she saw what it was.

"Dad! Dad! Remember when you said I could have a kitten? I think my kitten just found me."

1–11
12–23
24
25–37
38–39
40–51
52–65
66–76
77–87
88–94
95–105
106–112

**EVALUATING CODES
FOR ORAL FLUENCY**

sky   (/) words read incorrectly

blue

^   sky   (^) inserted word

        ( ]) after the last word

READING RATE AND ACCURACY

Total Words Read: _____

Number of Errors: _____

Number of Correct Words
Read Per Minute (WPM):   _____

Accuracy Rate: _____

(Number of Correct Words Read per
Minute ÷ Total Words Read)

READING FLUENCY

	Low	Average	High
Decoding ability	○	○	○
Pace	○	○	○
Syntax	○	○	○
Self-correction	○	○	○
Intonation	○	○	○

Record student rates on the Oral Fluency Scores pages.

Name _____ Date _____ Score _____

There's a Big Beautiful World Out There!/Night Comes

Comprehension and Vocabulary

Read the following questions carefully. Then completely fill in the bubble of each correct answer. You may look back at the selection to find the answer to each of the questions.

1. The story says that hiding under the covers
   Ⓐ is the best thing to do.
   Ⓑ makes you hungry.
   Ⓒ can be scary.
   Ⓓ gets boring.

2. The dog in the story
   Ⓐ is big and runs fast.
   Ⓑ looks mean but might be nice.
   Ⓒ has spots and is small.
   Ⓓ likes to bark and howl.

3. In the story, who will say everything will be all right?
   Ⓐ sister
   Ⓑ brother
   Ⓒ mother
   Ⓓ father

There's a Big Beautiful World Out There!/Night Comes (continued)

4. The story says you will miss out on the big beautiful world if you
   A go outside.
   B read the news.
   C ride a roller coaster.
   D hide under the covers.

5. Which of these is NOT in "Night Comes"?
   A stars
   B moon
   C clouds
   D night

6. The person who wrote "Night Comes"
   A is sleeping.
   B is a little hungry.
   C is tired.
   D is not afraid.

There's a Big Beautiful World Out There!/Night Comes (continued)

7. The stars come **peeking**. What does **peeking** mean?

- Ⓐ looking quickly
- Ⓑ hiding behind clouds
- Ⓒ staring for a long time
- Ⓓ smiling down

8. A **solo** can make you feel good. What is a **solo?**

- Ⓐ jumping high
- Ⓑ playing hard
- Ⓒ running or walking fast
- Ⓓ singing or playing alone

Read the following question carefully. Use a complete sentence to answer the question. Possible answer below

9. What does the story want you to do?

<u>The story wants you to stop being afraid and do things that are fun.</u>

10. Personal Response Write about something you used to be afraid of.

_____

_____

_____

_____

There's a Big Beautiful World Out There!/Night Comes (continued)

Phonics Review

Fill in the bubble under the word that fits in the blank and is spelled correctly.

Teacher: Fill in the bubble under the word that fits in the blank and is spelled correctly.

Teacher: May I play with that toy? Fill in the bubble under toy.

1. May I play with that _____?

toy	tou	tey	toie
●	○	○	○

Teacher: Did the water boil yet? Fill in the bubble under boil.

2. Did the water _____ yet?

bool	boil	boyl	bowle
○	●	○	○

Teacher: A lion's roar is loud. Fill in the bubble under loud.

3. A lion's roar is _____.

lood	loud	lowd	luod
○	●	○	○

Teacher: Bill lives in town. Fill in the bubble under town.

4. Bill lives in _____.

toon	toiwn	touen	town
○	○	○	●

Teacher: Open your mouth wide. Fill in the bubble under mouth.

5. Open your _____ wide.

meuth	mowth	mouth	moith
○	○	●	○

There's a Big Beautiful World Out There!/Night Comes (continued)

Grammar, Usage, and Mechanics

Read each item. Fill in the bubble for the answer you think is correct.

1. Which of these is a declarative sentence?
   - Ⓐ Is this your pet?
   - Ⓑ Don't do that.
   - **Ⓒ** Sue kicks the ball.
   - Ⓓ She scored a goal!

2. Which of these is an interrogative sentence?
   - **Ⓐ** Is it time to leave?
   - Ⓑ Ross wants to play, too.
   - Ⓒ Let Andy bat first.
   - Ⓓ The game is almost over.

3. Which of these is an exclamatory sentence?
   - Ⓐ Do you know her name?
   - **Ⓑ** I can't wait!
   - Ⓒ The train comes at five o'clock.
   - Ⓓ Her pencil is new.

4. Which of these is an imperative sentence?
   - **Ⓐ** Pick up that trash now.
   - Ⓑ Julie wants Hannah for her team.
   - Ⓒ Who is on the other team?
   - Ⓓ The path goes to the beach.

5. Which of these is a declarative sentence?
   - Ⓐ Please help Rita carry that.
   - Ⓑ Where is the train station?
   - **Ⓒ** Phan packed her bags.
   - Ⓓ Does that store sell books?

There's a Big Beautiful World Out There!/Night Comes (continued)

Oral Fluency Assessment

A Helpful Ship

A tug is small boat. It does an important job. It helps big	1–13
ships. Big ships carry things across the seas. They have to go	14–25
close to shore to unload. The big ships must sail into small	26–37
places. They do not know the places well. They could run into	38–49
danger.	50
The tug can push or pull the big ship. It will help the ship get	51–65
to the dock. The tug will make sure nothing bad happens.	66–76
Tugs are strong and work hard. A small tug can move a big ship.	77–90
With the help of a tug, a large ship will get into the harbor	91–104
and finish its job.	105–108

EVALUATING CODES FOR ORAL FLUENCY

sky   (/) words read incorrectly

blue
  ^   sky   (^) inserted word
              ( ]) after the last word

READING RATE AND ACCURACY

Total Words Read: _____

Number of Errors: _____

Number of Correct Words
Read Per Minute (WPM): _____

Accuracy Rate: _____

(Number of Correct Words Read per
Minute ÷ Total Words Read)

READING FLUENCY

	Low	Average	High
Decoding ability	○	○	○
Pace	○	○	○
Syntax	○	○	○
Self-correction	○	○	○
Intonation	○	○	○

Record student rates on the Oral Fluency Scores pages.

Name _____ **Date** _____ **Score** _____

Clyde Monster/The Cat and the Mice

Comprehension and Vocabulary

Read the following questions carefully. Then completely fill in the bubble of each correct answer. You may look back at the selection to find the answer to each of the questions.

1. You know the story is not real because
   Ⓐ monsters are not clumsy.
   Ⓑ monsters are not ugly.
   Ⓒ monsters do not exist.
   Ⓓ monsters do turn somersaults.

2. What is Clyde afraid of?
   Ⓐ dogs
   Ⓑ people
   Ⓒ loud noises
   Ⓓ bright lights

3. Something that is real and not make-believe in the story is
   Ⓐ a pretty monster.
   Ⓑ a family of monsters.
   Ⓒ being able to breathe fire.
   Ⓓ being afraid of the dark.

Clyde Monster/The Cat and the Mice (continued)

4. Clyde is different because he is

Ⓐ hungrier than other monsters.

Ⓑ funnier than other monsters.

Ⓒ clumsier than other monsters.

Ⓓ scarier than other monsters.

5. Why is the cat chasing the mice?

Ⓐ The cat is sad.

Ⓑ The cat wants to play.

Ⓒ The cat has no friends.

Ⓓ The cat is hungry.

6. No one answers the oldest mouse's question because

Ⓐ the mice are too scared.

Ⓑ no one heard it.

Ⓒ the question is too hard.

Ⓓ they are afraid of the oldest mouse.

Clyde Monster/The Cat and the Mice (continued)

7. Many mice had something to **suggest**. To **suggest** means to

    (A) say.

    (B) run.

    (C) hide.

    (D) sleep.

8. Monsters are **usually** ugly. **Usually** means

    (A) most of the time.

    (B) in a dark room.

    (C) only when angry.

    (D) never.

Read the following question carefully. Use a complete sentence to answer the question. Possible answer below

9. What does Clyde's father show him?

Father shows Clyde that there are no people in his cave.

10. **Personal Response** What do you do to feel safe at night?

_____

_____

_____

_____

Clyde Monster/The Cat and the Mice (continued)

Phonics Review

Fill in the bubble under the word that fits in the blank and is spelled correctly.

Teacher: Fill in the bubble under the word that fits in the blank and is spelled correctly.

Teacher: Ben <u>unties</u> his shoe. Fill in the bubble under <u>unties</u>.

1. Ben _____ his shoe.

intiez	ontiez	unties	anties
○	○	●	○

Teacher: Ana <u>batted</u> first. Fill in the bubble under <u>batted</u>.

2. Ana _____ first.

batted	baated	batd	batteed
●	○	○	○

Teacher: Are you <u>asking</u> me? Fill in the bubble under <u>asking</u>.

3. Are you _____ me?

askking	asking	askng	askiing
○	●	○	○

Teacher: Thank you for your <u>kindness</u>. Fill in the bubble under <u>kindness</u>.

4. Thank you for your _____.

kindnss	kindeness	kindness	kindnes
○	○	●	○

Teacher: This story has two <u>parts</u>. Fill in the bubble under <u>parts</u>.

5. This story has two _____.

parttes	partts	partes	parts
○	○	○	●

Clyde Monster/The Cat and the Mice (continued)

Grammar, Usage, and Mechanics

Read each item. Fill in the bubble for the answer you think is correct.

1. Which sentence has correct capitalization?
   - Ⓐ Can i go along with you?
   - Ⓒ that's Riverside School.
   - Ⓑ Aunt Rita wants to leave.
   - Ⓓ The game is on monday.

2. Which sentence has correct capitalization?
   - Ⓐ Grandpa lives in Denver, Colorado.
   - Ⓑ Grandma sent a package to florida.
   - Ⓒ did you ever visit Africa?
   - Ⓓ My friend's family is from korea.

3. Which sentence has correct capitalization?
   - Ⓐ our first game is on monday.
   - Ⓑ His Birthday is on sunday.
   - Ⓒ My birthday is in April.
   - Ⓓ The first snow was in november.

4. Which sentence has correct punctuation?
   - Ⓐ Dad was born on April 24, 1973.
   - Ⓑ Dad was born on April 24 1973.
   - Ⓒ Dad was born on April, 24 1973.
   - Ⓓ Dad was born on April, 24, 1973.

5. Which sentence has correct capitalization and punctuation?
   - Ⓐ Flora lives in austin, Texas.
   - Ⓑ Flora lives in Austin, Texas.
   - Ⓒ Flora lives in Austin texas.
   - Ⓓ Flora lives in austin, texas.

Clyde Monster/The Cat and the Mice (continued)

Oral Fluency Assessment

Rainy Day

It was a rainy day. The children were sad. They could not go	1–13
out to play. They had to stay home. They did not know what	14–26
they would do. They sat around bored.	27–33
Mom saw how unhappy they were. She told them not to	34–44
forget what they could do inside. They could read books.	45–54
They could play games. Maybe they could watch a movie.	55–64
The children said that would be fun.	65–71
Soon Mom made lunch. The children imagined it was a	72–81
picnic. They ate on the porch. They put a blanket down to make	82–94
it seem real.	95–97
The sun soon came out. But no one noticed. They were	98–108
having fun inside.	109–111

**EVALUATING CODES
FOR ORAL FLUENCY**

sky ~~(/)~~ (/) words read incorrectly

blue
^ sky (^) inserted word
( ]) after the last word

READING RATE AND ACCURACY

Total Words Read: _____

Number of Errors: _____

Number of Correct Words
Read Per Minute (WPM): _____

Accuracy Rate: _____

(Number of Correct Words Read per
Minute ÷ Total Words Read)

READING FLUENCY

	Low	Average	High
Decoding ability	○	○	○
Pace	○	○	○
Syntax	○	○	○
Self-correction	○	○	○
Intonation	○	○	○

Record student rates on the Oral Fluency Scores pages.

Ira Sleeps Over

Comprehension and Vocabulary

Read the following questions carefully. Then completely fill in the bubble of each correct answer. You may look back at the selection to find the answer to each of the questions.

1. This story is mostly about
   - Ⓐ things that are fun to do at a sleep-over.
   - Ⓑ why boys like teddy bears.
   - Ⓒ a boy who sleeps over at a friend's house.
   - Ⓓ two boys who want the same toy.

2. What does Ira do right after Reggie said "Foo Foo"?
   - Ⓐ He tells a scary story about ghosts.
   - Ⓑ He tries to wake up Reggie.
   - Ⓒ He falls asleep.
   - Ⓓ He goes home and gets his teddy bear.

3. Ira does not take his teddy bear to Reggie's house because
   - Ⓐ he thinks Reggie will laugh.
   - Ⓑ the bear is too big.
   - Ⓒ his sister will tease him.
   - Ⓓ Reggie says he has a bear.

Ira Sleeps Over (continued)

4. Why is Ira excited at the start of the story?

 Ⓐ He gets a brand new toy.

 Ⓑ He will be doing something new.

 Ⓒ He meets a new friend.

 Ⓓ He is going to a new school.

5. Which of these is true about Ira's sister?

 Ⓐ She thinks Ira is tall.

 Ⓑ She knows Reggie well.

 Ⓒ She takes care of Ira.

 Ⓓ She likes to tease Ira.

6. What is the name of Ira's teddy bear?

 Ⓐ Foo Foo

 Ⓑ Tah Tah

 Ⓒ Reggie

 Ⓓ Aroomp

Ira Sleeps Over (continued)

7. The boys wanted to have a wrestling **match.** A **match** is a kind of

Ⓐ game.

Ⓑ toy.

Ⓒ book.

Ⓓ bed.

8. Ira **changed his mind.** This means he

Ⓐ wanted something to eat.

Ⓑ did something different.

Ⓒ worried about something.

Ⓓ had a lot of fun.

Read the following question carefully. Use a complete sentence to answer the question. Possible answer below

9. Why does Ira decide it is okay to go and get his teddy bear?

Ira decides it is okay because Reggie has a teddy bear, too.

10. Personal Response What do you have that is like Ira's teddy bear?

_____

_____

_____

Ira Sleeps Over (continued)

Phonics Review

Fill in the bubble under the word that fits in the blank and is spelled correctly.

Teacher: Fill in the bubble under the word that fits in the blank and is spelled correctly.

Teacher: Will Kara go <u>with</u> you? Fill in the bubble under <u>with</u>.

1. Will Kara go _____ you?

wint	wigh	wich	with
○	○	○	●

Teacher: Peg lives <u>near</u> the park. Fill in the bubble under <u>near</u>.

2. Peg lives _____ the park.

nerr	near	neer	nair
○	●	○	○

Teacher: My brother lost one <u>sock</u>. Fill in the bubble under <u>sock</u>.

3. My brother lost one _____.

sock	soct	sosk	soch
●	○	○	○

Teacher: That <u>sound</u> is loud. Fill in the bubble under <u>sound</u>.

4. That _____ is loud.

sound	sownd	soind	soond
●	○	○	○

Teacher: Jim <u>took</u> his cat outside. Fill in the bubble under <u>took</u>.

5. Jim _____ his cat outside.

toik	touk	took	tok
○	○	●	○

Ira Sleeps Over (continued)

Grammar, Usage, and Mechanics

Read each item. Fill in the bubble for the answer you think is correct.

1. Which of these means the same as <u>are not</u>?

Ⓐ isn't   Ⓒ don't

Ⓑ aren't   Ⓓ can't

2. Which of these means the same as <u>they will</u>?

Ⓐ they'

Ⓑ they're

Ⓒ they'll

Ⓓ we'll

3. Which of these means the same as <u>you are</u>?

Ⓐ you're

Ⓑ you'll

Ⓒ he'll

Ⓓ we're

4. Which of these means the same as <u>would not</u>?

Ⓐ won't

Ⓑ wasn't

Ⓒ wouldn't

Ⓓ we'll

5. Which of these means the same as <u>he is</u>?

Ⓐ she'll

Ⓑ he's

Ⓒ he'd

Ⓓ it's

Ira Sleeps Over (continued)

Oral Fluency Assessment

A Sense of Smell

Dogs have good noses. Dogs can smell things that people can not smell. They use their noses to find food.	1–10 11–20
Sometimes dogs help find people who are lost. They follow them by sniffing the trail. They put their noses low to the ground. They smell where the people walked. Dogs help to save lots of people. They can find animals, too.	21–30 31–42 43–53 54–61
Dogs learned to smell well long ago. It helped them find food. It helped them find other dogs. A group of dogs is called a pack. If a dog was lost, it could smell the pack. Then the dog could find its way home.	62–72 73–85 86–100 101–105

**EVALUATING CODES
FOR ORAL FLUENCY**

sky   (/) words read incorrectly

blue

^   sky   (^) inserted word

( ]) after the last word

READING RATE AND ACCURACY

Total Words Read: _____

Number of Errors: _____

Number of Correct Words
Read Per Minute (WPM):   _____

Accuracy Rate: _____

(Number of Correct Words Read per
Minute ÷ Total Words Read)

READING FLUENCY

	Low	Average	High
Decoding ability	○	○	○
Pace	○	○	○
Syntax	○	○	○
Self-correction	○	○	○
Intonation	○	○	○

Record student rates on the Oral Fluency Scores pages.

Name _____ **Date** _____ **Score** _____

Writing Prompt

Narrative Writing

Writing Situation

Your own adventure story

Audience

Other students your age

Directions for Writing

Write your own adventure story. It can be in a real or imaginary setting like a different planet or a time in the past. Your story should have interesting characters and an exciting plot.

Checklist

You will earn the best score if you

- think about your ideas before you start writing.
- stay on topic.
- have a good beginning, middle, and end to your story.
- tell about the place where the story happens.
- tell about the characters in your story.
- write complete sentences.
- use words that tell how the characters feel.
- include enough details so the reader will understand what happened.
- use correct capital letters, end marks, and spelling.
- read your writing after you finish and check for mistakes.

Four Point Rubrics for Narrative Writing

Genre	1 Point	2 Points	3 Points	4 Points
Narrative	Narrative has missing details or elements. Order and narrative structure are lacking. Plot is unclear. Character development is not apparent. Setting does not include descriptions of where and when the narrative is set.	Narrative includes plot outline and some descriptive details, but narrative structure is not entirely clear. Character development is minimal. Setting includes minimal descriptions.	Narrative includes fairly well developed plot. Narrative structure is clear. Characters are developed, though some characters may seem superficial. Setting includes description.	Narrative includes complex, organized plot line(s). Narrative structure is well defined. Characters well defined throughout. Setting includes detailed descriptions.
Narrative: Theme	No theme is apparent.	Superficial theme is included but not integrated.	A theme is expressed but not well developed.	The narrative fully develops a theme that expresses an underlying message beyond the narrative plot.
Writing Traits				
Audience	Displays little or no sense of audience.	Displays some sense of audience.	Writes with audience in mind throughout.	Displays a strong sense of audience. Engages audience.
Voice	The writing provides little sense of voice.	The voice is either inappropriately personal or inappropriately impersonal.	A voice is present, though in places, the writing is less expressive, engaging, or sincere.	The writer has chosen a voice appropriate for the topic, purpose, and audience.
Writing Conventions				
Conventions Overall	Demonstrates little evidence of standard writing conventions.	Demonstrates limited but inconsistent control of standard writing conventions.	Demonstrates emerging, consistent use of standard writing conventions such as capitalization and end punctuation.	Demonstrates consistent use and awareness of standard writing conventions.

Six Point Rubrics

Use the following rubrics to assess student writing.

6 Points

The writing is focused, purposeful, and reflects insight into the writing situation. The paper conveys a sense of completeness and wholeness with adherence to the main idea, and its organizational pattern provides for a logical progression of ideas. The support is substantial, specific, relevant, concrete, and/or illustrative. The paper demonstrates a commitment to and an involvement with the subject, clarity in presentation of ideas, and may use creative writing strategies appropriate to the purpose of the paper. The writing demonstrates a mature command of language (word choice) with freshness of expression. Sentence structure is varied, and sentences are complete except when fragments are used purposefully. Few, if any, convention errors occur in mechanics, usage, and punctuation.

5 Points

The writing focuses on the topic, and its organizational pattern provides for a progression of ideas, although some lapses may occur. The paper conveys a sense of completeness or wholeness. The support is ample. The writing demonstrates a mature command of language, including precise word choice. There is variation in sentence structure, and, with rare exceptions, sentences are complete except when fragments are used purposefully. The paper generally follows the conventions of mechanics, usage, and spelling.

4 Points

The writing is generally focused on the topic but may include extraneous or loosely related material. An organizational pattern is apparent, although some lapses may occur. The paper exhibits some sense of completeness or wholeness. The support, including word choice, is adequate, although development may be uneven. There is little variation in sentence structure, and most sentences are complete. The paper generally follows the conventions of mechanics, usage, and spelling.

3 Points

The writing is generally focused on the topic but may include extraneous or loosely related material. An organizational pattern has been attempted, but the paper may lack a sense of completeness or wholeness. Some support is included, but developemt is erratic. Word choice is adequate but may be limited, predictable, or occasionally vague. There is little, if any, variation in sentence structure. Knowledge of the conventions of mechanics and usage is usually demonstrated, and commonly used words are usually spelled correctly.

2 Points

The writing is related to the topic but includes extraneous or loosely related material. Little evidence of an organizational pattern may be demonstrated, and the paper may lack a sense of completeness or wholeness. Development of support is inadequate or illogical. Word choice is limited, inappropriate, or vague. There is little, if any, variation in sentence structure, and gross errors in sentence structure may occur. Errors in basic conventions of mechanics and usage may occur, and commonly used words may be misspelled.

1 Point

The writing may only minimally address the topic. The paper is fragmentary or incoherent listing of related ideas or sentences or both. Little, if any, development of support or an organizational pattern or both is apparent. Limited or inappropriate word choice may obscure meaning. Gross errors in sentence structure and usage may impede communication. Frequent and blatant errors may occur in the basic conventions of mechanics and usage, and commonly used words may be misspelled.

Unscorable

The paper is unscorable because

- the response is not related to what the prompt requested the student to do.
- the response is simply a rewording of the prompt
- the response is a copy of a published work.
- the student refused to write.
- the response is illegible.
- the response is incomprehensible (words are arrange in such a way that no meaning is conveyed).
- the response contains an insufficient amount of writing to determine if the student was attempting to address the prompt.

Oral Fluency Scores

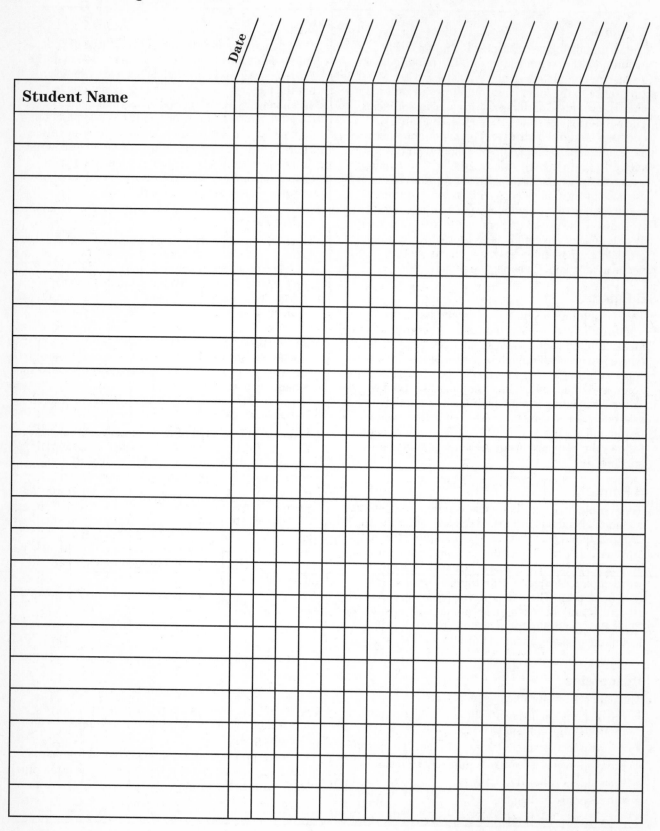

Student Name	Date															

Oral Fluency Scores

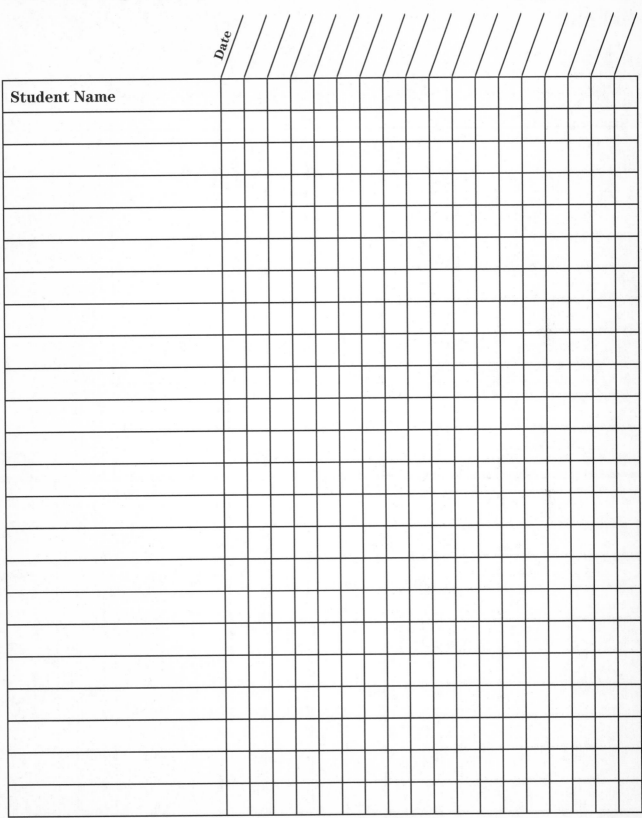

Student Name	Date															

Class Assessment Record

Student Name	Unit 7, Lessons 1–5	Unit 7, Lessons 6–10	Unit 7, Lessons 11–15	Unit 7, Lessons 16–20	Unit 7 Writing Prompt	Unit 8, Lessons 1–5	Unit 8, Lessons 6–10	Unit 8, Lessons 11–15	Unit 8, Lessons 16–20	Unit 8, Lessons 21–25	Unit 8 Writing Prompt

Class Assessment Record

Student Name	Unit 9, Lessons 1–5	Unit 9, Lessons 6–10	Unit 9, Lessons 11–15	Unit 9, Lessons 16–20	Unit 9, Lessons 21–25	Unit 9 Writing Prompt	Unit 10, Lessons 1–5	Unit 10, Lessons 6–10	Unit 10, Lessons 11–15	Unit 10, Lessons 16–20	Unit 10 Writing Prompt

Student Assessment Record

Name _____

Teacher _____ Grade _____

Unit/ Lesson	Assessment Section	Date	Number Possible	Number Right	%	Score (Rubrics/WPM)

Comprehension Observation Log

Student _____ **Date** _____

Unit _____ **Lesson** _____ **Selection Title** _____

General Comprehension
Concepts discussed: _____
_____

Behavior Within a Group
Articulates, expresses ideas: _____
_____

Joins discussions: _____
_____

Collaborates (such as *works well with other students, works alone*): _____
_____

Role in Group
Role (such as *leader, summarizer, questioner, critic, observer, non-participant*): _____
_____

Flexibility (changes roles when necessary): _____
_____

Use of Reading Strategies
Uses strategies when needed (either those taught or student's choice of strategy)/Describes strategies used:
_____
_____
_____

Changes strategies when appropriate: _____
_____

Changes Since Last Observation
_____
_____
_____